Geographical Case Studies

THE UNITED KINGDOM

Chris Burnett, Keith Flinders and Barnaby Lenon

Hodder & Stoughton

A MEMBER OF THE HODDER HEADLINE GROUP

Acknowledgements

The authors and publishers would like to thank the following for permission to reproduce materials in this book. Every effort has been made to trace and acknowledge all copyright holders, but if any have been overlooked the publishers will be pleased to make the necessary arrangements.

Mohammed Iftikhar Ali of Lye; Birmingham International Airport, Derek Edwards; British School, Jakarta, Frank Clarke; Central Statistical Office, Figures 1.4, 8.1, 10.1–4; Commission for the New Towns, Central Milton Keynes, MK9 3HS, Figure 7.7; Geographical Association, Figures 6.1–5; HarperCollins Cartographic, Figure 7.11; Hucknall National School, Steve Sibley and Louise Dobbs; Imperial Park, Newport, Figure 8.29; Merry Hill Centre, Figure 8.23; Old Castle Books, Figure 7.10; OPCS, Figure 6.9; Ordnance Survey, © Crown Copyright, Figures 7.15, 6.8, 8.14; Ordnance Survey of Northern Ireland with the permission of the Director and Chief Executive © Crown Copyright, Figure 10.5; Philip Allan Publishers, *Geography Review*, Vol 7 No 2, Figures 5.2, 5.5, 5.7; Railway Development School, Douglas Smart; Redhill School, P Lloyd Jones; Reed Consumer Books, Figures 4.2, 4.3; Routledge, *Urban and Regional Planning*, P Hall, Figure 7.6; Strathclyde Regional Council, Jim Mearns, Figure 9.1; Sustrans, Les Tombs.

The publishers would also like to thank the following for giving permission to reproduce copyright photographs in this book.

J Allan Cash, Figures 5.3, 7.19. 10.7, 10.13; Martin Bond/Science Photo Library, Figure 11.15; British Coal, Figure 11.10; Robert Eames/Impact, Figure 11.8; Roger Hutchings/Network, Figure 7.8; Jefferson's Air Photography, Figure 9.11; Landform Slides, Figure 4.4; Montupet Ltd, Figure 10.9; Ann Muller, Figure 7.15a; National Rivers Authority, Figure 2.11; Severn Trent Water, Figures 11.4, 11.5; © Drew Gardner, Sunday Telegraph 1994, Figure 3.8; Telegraph, Figure 11.20; Thames Water, Figure 7.21; Bob Turner/Trip, Figure 10.14; John Sturrock/Network, Figure 10.8; Trip Photography, Figures 2.9, 7.18; University of Hull, Figures 3.7, 3.9; Heather Wilson, Figure 5.5.

All other photos belong to the authors.

Cover artwork by Angela Wood.

Inside artwork by Jillian Luff, Bitmap Graphics, Berkhamsted.

British Library Cataloguing in Publication Data

Burnett, Chris
Geographical Case Studies: United Kingdom
I. Title
914.1

ISBN 0-340-63105-8

First published 1995

Impression number	10	9	8	7	6	5	4	3	2	1
Year	1999		1998		1997		1996		1995	

Typeset by Wearset, Boldon, Tyne and Wear.
Printed in Malaysia for Hodder & Stoughton Educational, a division of Hodder Headline Plc, 338 Euston Road, London NW1 3BH by Times Offset (M) Sdn Bhd.

Contents

Issues that are referred to elsewhere in the text are marked with this symbol: ◆3, giving the relevant page number

1 regional contrasts

WHAT IS BRITAIN?

If you asked ten people what we mean when we talk about *Britain* you would get several different answers. The reason is that there is no agreed definition of Britain. We can agree, however, on the definition of three terms which you will know.

The British Isles: England, Wales, Scotland, Isle of Man, Channel Islands, and all of Ireland. This is a geographical area, not a country.

Great Britain: England, Wales, and Scotland.

The United Kingdom: England, Wales, Scotland, Northern Ireland, Isle of Man, and the Channel Isles – this is the area governed by Parliament in Westminster.

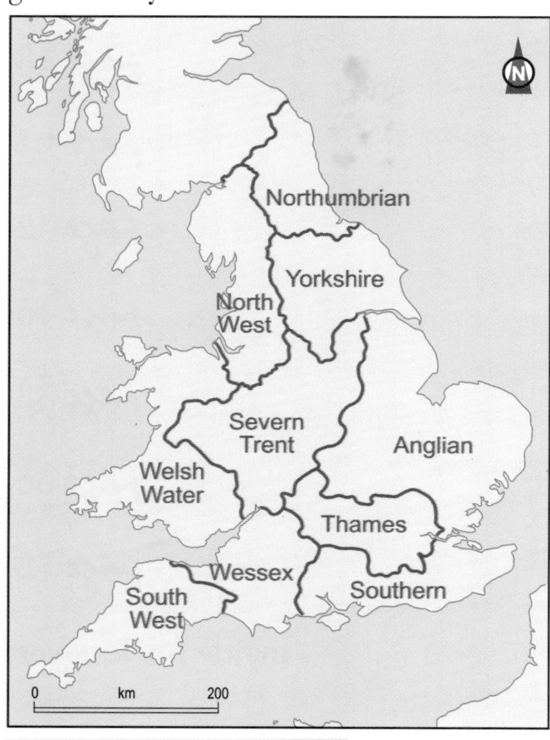

Figure 1.1 Water authorities

1 Look at Figures 1.1, 1.2, 1.4 and 6.1 (page 21). For each map say whether the area shown is the British Isles, Great Britain, the United Kingdom, or none of these.

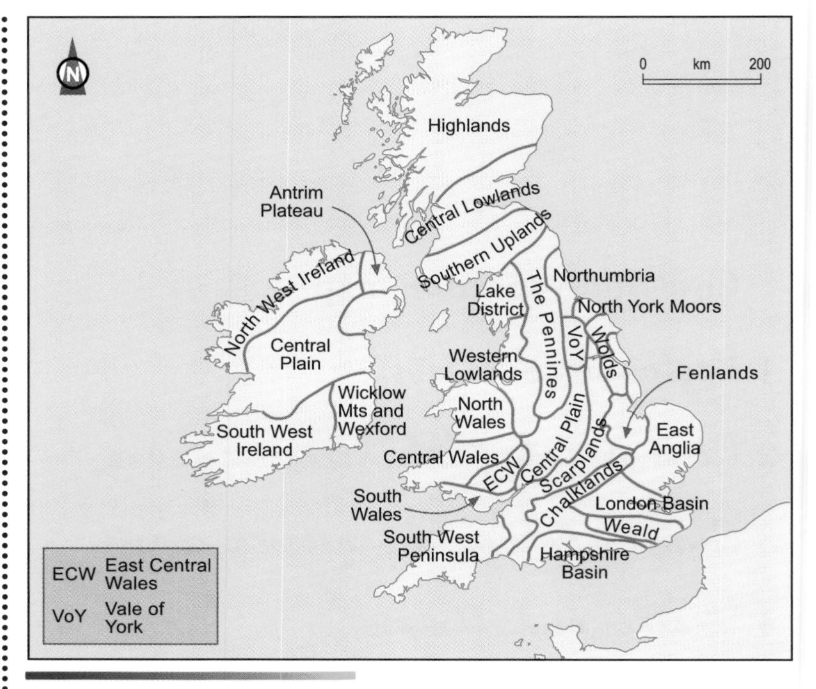

Figure 1.2 Physical regions

HOW CAN WE DIVIDE BRITAIN?

Most people have a sense of belonging to a particular geographical area – a house, a street, a neighbourhood, a town, a region of the country. Sometimes this sense of belonging leads people to support a particular sports team.

2 How does the region where you live differ from other parts of Britain? Answer the following questions about the characteristics of the region in which you live.

- **a** What landscapes are typical of the area? Is it flat, hilly or mountainous?
- **b** Do most people live in a city, in towns or in villages?
- **c** Is the area very old, or is much of the building new?
- **d** Name two important industries or activities in which many people work.
- **e** What do you like and dislike about the region where you live?
- **f** Are there any other aspects of the area which make it different from other parts of Britain?

3 Which independent TV region (channel 3) are you in? Watch channel 3 between about 5.15 and 7.00 pm. How do the news and weather forecast take into account the interests particular to your region?

Figure 1.2 is a map of the **physical regions** of the British Isles – each area has a particular type of landscape or combination of landscapes. Figure 1.1 shows the **Water Authorities** of England and Wales. The Water Authorities are responsible for looking after our rivers as well as water supply and sewerage. It was felt that it would make life unnecessarily difficult if larger river systems were divided amongst two or more Authorities, so these regions are based on river basins. The regional division which is best known is that used for **local government**. The smallest units in which people are elected to represent us are called **parishes**. If you live in a village you are probably very aware of the local parish council and the activities it organises. Bigger in size than a parish is the **district**, which manages planning and some local services. Finally, both parishes and districts are grouped together to make up **counties**

Regions of the UK	Mean annual temperature	Mean annual rainfall	Population, mid- 1990s	Unemployment mid-1990s	Land farmed	Average weekly house-hold income	Regional income from services	Male employees in manufacturing
	°C	mm	mill	%	%	£	%	%
England								
North	8	1000	3.1	11	39	285	58	32
North West	9	850	6.4	10	22	317	62	32
Yorkshire and Humberside	9	650	4.9	9	42	303	60	33
West Midlands	9	700	5.3	9	42	304	58	40
East Midlands	10	600	4.1	7	49	344	57	38
East Anglia	10	500	2.1	6	54	350	63	28
South West	10	900	4.7	7	56	346	66	27
South East (includes London)	10	700	17.6	7	33	407	75	20
Wales	9	1200	2.9	9	30	295	59	31
Scotland	7	1400	5.1	10	25	314	64	25
Northern Ireland	9	1100	1.6	16	48	281	66	24

Figure 1.3 Data for the standard regions

The maps on the inside front cover and in Figure 6.1 (page 21) show the county boundaries of Great Britain. The present pattern of counties was established in 1974, and has recently been reviewed and further modified by the government. Two types of changes were made.

- The first idea was to abolish some district councils in England and Wales and to give their functions to the county councils: one authority to replace two. This might make the system more efficient.
- The second plan was to alter the boundaries of some counties, in order to destroy unpopular counties altogether and create some new ones. To decide the new counties the planners found out the views of local people. This takes us back to the beginning of this chapter – the idea of a sense of place, the region to which people feel they belong.

Figure 1.4 The standard regions

DO REGIONS DIFFER?

Figure 1.4 shows the **standard regions** of the UK. These are the units used for collecting statistics and information. Some of these statistics are given in Figure 1.3.

4 Study the table in Figure 1.3. Choose any two columns and draw a bar graph to show the data. Write a description of the differences you observe between regions.

5 Which standard region is your home in? Is your home area typical of the standard region in which it is located?

The statistics for the standard regions bring out some of the differences between different parts of the UK: contrasts in physical geography, which are highlighted in Chapters 2–5 of this book; the high unemployment in Northern Ireland; and the greater impact of farming in the South West and East Anglia. Regions such as these also have big contrasts *within* them – in fact, there are far bigger contrasts within regions than between them. The South East region has relatively low unemployment, but areas of London have amongst the highest unemployment in the country. It is the contrasts between and within regions that this book concentrates on.

Landforms and processes of a river valley: a case study of the River Wyre, Lancashire

All rivers are different, and yet they do all have similar characteristics.

All rivers carry rainwater which falls on a certain area of land and travels downhill towards the sea. The area of land which it drains is called a **drainage basin**. The drainage basin of every river is a different size and shape, although the highest land is always around its edges.

Figure 2.1 shows a river drainage basin and the other features which are found on most rivers.

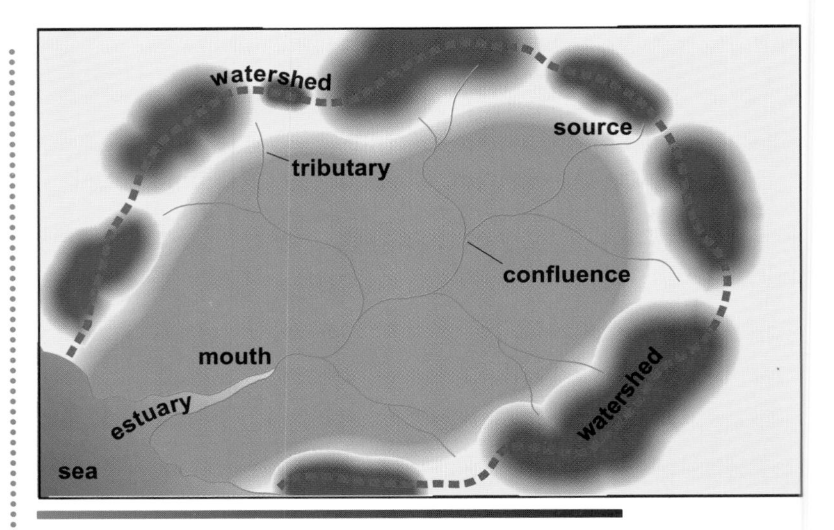

Figure 2.1 The characteristics of a drainage basin

Figure 2.2

Figure 2.3

Figure 2.4

Figure 2.5

Figure 2.6 Figure 2.7

Figures 2.2–2.7 Sites on the River Wyre

1 Study Figure 2.1 which shows the characteristic features of a drainage basin. Match up the following heads with the correct tails in the table.

HEADS	TAILS
The estuary of a river is	where the river enters a lake, reservoir or the sea
The watershed is	called a tributary
A river's mouth is	the area of a river beyond the mouth, going seawards
Where two streams or rivers meet is	called its source
A small stream joining the main river is	the boundary of higher land around the drainage basin
The start of a river is	called a confluence

2 The photographs in Figures 2.2–2.7 were taken at the locations marked on Figure 2.8. Make a list to show which photograph was taken at each of the locations A–F.

3 Using Figure 2.8, answer the following questions.
   a Where is the source of the River Wyre?
   b Which town is at the mouth of the Wyre?
   c Into which sea area does the river flow?
   d Does more rain fall at the mouth or the source of the River Wyre?

4 Study the photographs in Figures 2.2–2.7 again, copy out these sentences, and state whether they are true or false, and why.
   a The river valley becomes wider downstream.
   b The river valley becomes steeper downstream.
   c The river has embankments to stop it flooding its valley in the hills.
   d People have not changed the course of the river.

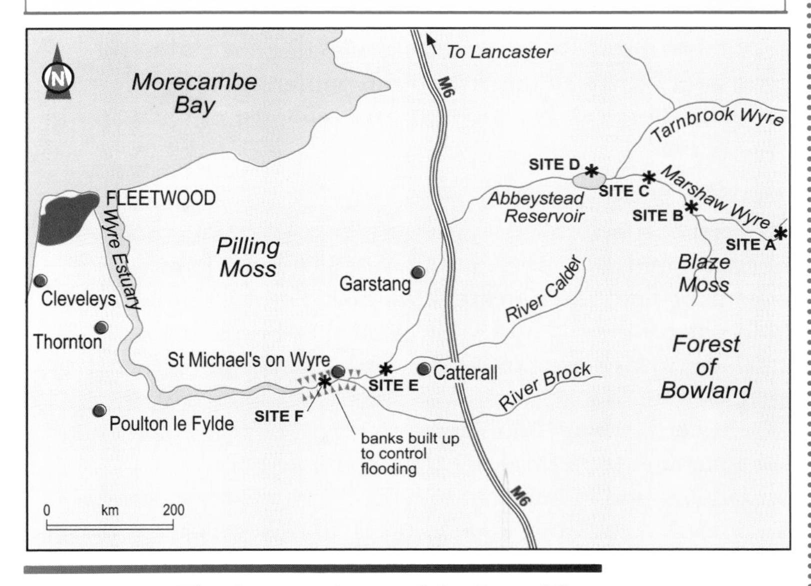

Figure 2.8 The drainage basin of the River Wyre

THE RIVER WYRE: A TYPICAL RIVER IN THE UK

Figures 2.2–2.7 were all taken at different points in the valley of the River Wyre. This river has its source in the hills of the Forest of Bowland and flows to its mouth at Morecambe Bay, part of the Irish Sea (Figure 2.8). The photographs show how the shape of the river valley and channel change as the river flows from its source to its mouth.

THE WORK OF RIVERS

The River Wyre, like all rivers, changes the landscape through which it flows in three ways. Moving water has energy which it uses to pick up and remove material from its banks and bed; this is called **erosion**. It **transports** this material, either dissolved in the water (**solution**), mixed in with the water (**suspension**) **or by** dragging it along the bed (**saltation**), until the load becomes too great for the river's energy. It then drops some of the material and this is called **deposition**.

Figures 2.2–2.7 show evidence of all three river processes: erosion, transportation and deposition.

5 Study Figures 2.2–2.7. In which photos can you see evidence of:
   a river erosion?
   b transportation processes?
   c river deposition?
6 Explain in your own words how a river carries its load by:
   a solution; b suspension; c saltation.
7 Look at Figure 2.3. Why is the water here and in other parts of the valley brown?
8 Using the information on these two pages write an explanation of 'How a river changes its valley'. Explain about the work it does and how this changes the shape of the valley between the source and the mouth.

Causes and effects of river flooding: a case study of the Chichester Floods, 1994

Figure 2.9 Flooding in Chichester

> TYPES OF FLOOD DEFENCE WORK CARRIED OUT BY THE NRA
>
> - Clear all channels of debris and silt.
> - Build higher and stronger river banks.
> - Pump water from low-lying land.
> - Build culverts to divert flood waters.
> - Major engineering projects.
> - Flood warning systems.
> - Manage flood control basins.

Figure 2.10 Flood defence work carried out by the NRA

1 a With a partner think of as many different things as you can that might cause a river to flood.

b Use the ideas from your whole class to make two lists. One list should be called 'Natural causes of flooding' and the other 'Ways that people affect flooding'.

2 a Explain what might have happened if the culvert in Chichester had failed.

b How had people's activities over the year made this flood more difficult to manage?

3 a Make a list of the main causes of the flood.

b For each cause, try to suggest a way to reduce its effect in the future.

WHAT IS A FLOOD?

A river floods when it is carrying more water than can be contained within its banks.

There are many reasons why rivers flood and water spills onto the land next to the river, which is called the **flood plain**. Sometimes several different factors all help to cause a river to flood; on other occasions only one thing causes the flood to occur. Some of the factors are completely natural but sometimes people have made changes to the environment, which have caused the floods or make the flooding worse.

FLOOD REPORT

For several months, the rainfall had been well above average over most of the United Kingdom. By the beginning of winter, the soil and the rocks below were completely saturated and could not absorb any more rainfall. Unfortunately, a long wet spell, caused by several depressions passing overhead in early January, caused serious flooding. 16

The source of the River Lavant, which flows through the town of Chichester, is a stream flowing out of the South Downs. These hills are mostly of chalk, which absorbs water easily. However in January 1994, the chalk was completely saturated by the heavy rainfall and many new springs broke out, adding to the flow of the river.

In Chichester, a flood retaining wall had been demolished the previous summer by contractors, who did not realise the river could carry so much water in winter. A clay and sandbag dam was quickly built to keep most of the water in the channel.

The river flows through the oldest parts of the city in an artificial channel, called a **culvert**. This passes under many buildings and can carry 5 m^3 of water per second, but on 5 January, flows were greater than that. The river burst its banks above the city and water flooded two main dual-carriageways, causing transport chaos. Sixteen army reserve fire engines were used to pump water from above the city to Chichester Harbour, 3 km away, to try to stop the culvert and sandbag dam from breaking. This continued until 30 January and did prevent some of the city from becoming inundated. A full evacuation of the south eastern part of the city was planned in case the culvert failed. This would have involved many residents being taken out of the city by a fleet of buses.

Controlling river flooding: a case study of the River Mersey

Figure 2.11 Flood waters in the Sale Ees flood storage basin

In the UK, the National Rivers Authority (NRA) has the role of trying to prevent floods. This organisation gets its money from water licences, local councils and the national Government. It also has the job of controlling pollution and protecting all water environments, ensuring that there is enough clean water where it is needed. There are many different things which can be done to prevent floods (Figure 2.10), but it is not possible to stop *all* floods.

FLOOD DEFENCE

The section of the River Mersey between Stockport and Irlam Weir, where it joins the Manchester Ship Canal, meanders across a wide flood plain, which it has flooded on many occasions. For years, as the city of Manchester was growing, most of the flood plain was not used for building but for golf courses, sewage works and landfill rubbish tips. In recent years, as the city has continued to grow, more and more houses, schools, industries and other buildings have been built close to or on the flood plain.

In the 1970s, the M63 motorway was built along the Mersey Valley. Huge amounts of gravel were taken from the flood plain at Sale Ees to be used for building materials. This left a huge water-filled hole, which has been turned into Sale Water Park, a water sports centre and nature reserve. This area is now owned by the NRA and is one of two flood basins designed to prevent large-scale flooding.

The Sale Water Park flood basin

When river recording gauges upstream show that flooding is expected, sluice gates near Jackson's Boat will be opened. This will allow flood water onto the open land around Sale Water Park. As the level of the river falls after the peak flow, the waters will drain back into the river downstream of the Bridgewater Canal aqueduct. It is expected that the basin will have to be used about once every ten years and it was last used in December 1991.

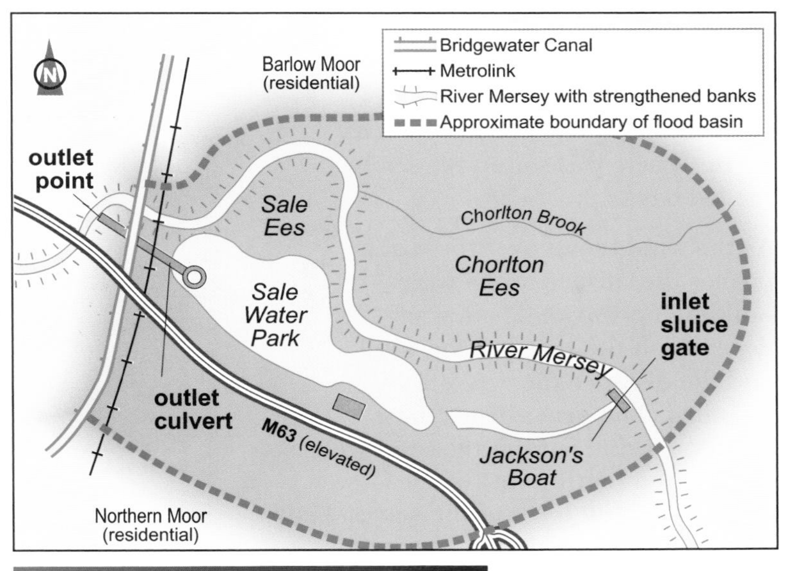

Figure 2.12 Sale Ees flood storage basin

1 Study the list of flood defence work (Figure 2.10) and for the first six examples, explain how this work will reduce flooding near rivers.

2 Use an atlas map and the information provided above to draw a sketch map similar to Figure 2.8, showing the drainage basin of the River Mersey. You should mark the following on your map: Pennine Hills; Stockport; Manchester Ship Canal; Warrington; Widnes; Liverpool; Irish Sea; Manchester; River Goyt; River Tame.

3 a Why was there no building on the flood plain of the River Mersey for many years?
  b Why is it being used for building now?

4 Make a copy of Figure 2.12 and add the following labels in the correct places to show how the flood basin works:
  a River level recording devices show flood levels are expected.
  b Inlet Sluice at Jackson's Boat is opened.
  c Flood waters fill the Water Park flood basin.
  d After peak flow water is returned to the river.

Coastal landforms: a case study of the Gower Peninsula

Do you like sandy beaches, rocks to climb on and caves to explore? The Gower Peninsula in South Wales has all of these – and more. Where the rock is hard, the cliffs can be as high as 50 m. Where it is softer, the sea has eroded bays.

As the wind blows over the sea, it pushes the surface of the water, building up waves. Their size depends on the speed of the wind and the distance the waves have travelled. The **prevailing** (most common) wind is from the southwest, so most of the south coast of the Gower receives the full force of the waves. Only bays at Oxwich and Port Eynon are sheltered from the worst storms by **headlands** of hard limestone. At the end of the headland at Rhossili, the coastguard has a distant view from the top of the 40 m high cliff. Down on the beach, there are still the remains of a shipwreck from 1897!

WAVES AT WORK

The water in a wave moves in a circle. Close to the coast, the sea-bed slows down the movement at the bottom of the circle. The surface of the wave is now moving fastest and crashes in as a breaker. Each wave can throw tonnes of water at the cliff and this squeezes the air in the cracks of the rock. This is called **hydraulic action**. Slowly the rock is shattered. The rock fragments are washed into the sea and waves may now throw them against the cliff again. This also breaks up the cliff and is called **abrasion**. From Oxwich to Worm's Head, the cliffs are made of Carboniferous Limestone, which is also under attack from the natural chemicals in the sea water.

Figure 3.1 Rhossili cliffs and Worm's Head. The remains of *The Helvetia* are still on the beach

Figure 3.2 The arch known as Devil's Bridge

1. Use your atlas to locate the Gower Peninsula. Which city is at its eastern end?
2. The distance which waves have travelled is called the **fetch**. If this is a long distance, winds can build up large waves. Use your atlas to identify the nearest land to the south west from the Gower Peninsula and measure the fetch of waves from this direction. (You will need a world map!)

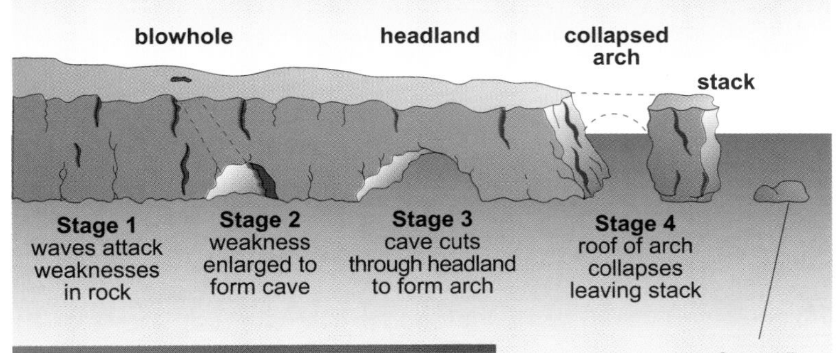

Figure 3.3 The sea erodes a headland

Where joints in the rock are exposed, or faults occur, the waves get to work and slowly produce a **cave**. The most famous cave in the Gower cliffs is Paviland Cave, formed between the ice ages when the sea-level was higher. It was lived in 18 500 years ago! If a cave reaches up to the surface of the headland, it forms a hole through which a breaking wave can send out a blast of air and sea spray, like a whale does. This feature is called a **blowhole**. The west end of Worm's Head has one and nearby a cave has cut right through to form an **arch** known as Devil's Bridge (Figure 3.2). Eventually the roof of the arch will collapse and the tip of Worm's Head will become an isolated rock known as a **stack**. In fact the whole of Worm's Head is really a large stack. At high tide it is an island, but for four hours around low tide, it is possible to walk across the shore from Rhossili. This rough, rocky surface is called a **wave-cut platform**.

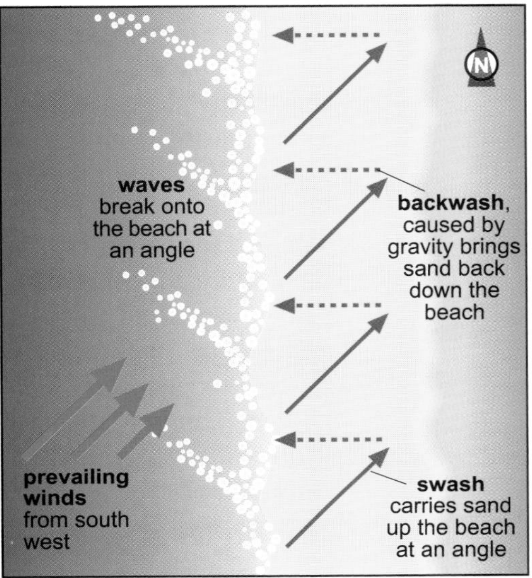

Figure 3.4 Longshore drift on Rhossili Beach

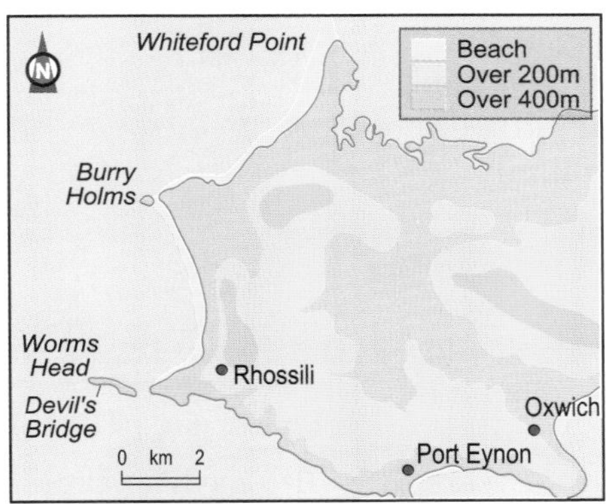

Figure 3.5 The western part of the Gower Peninsula

3 Look at Figure 3.2. The tallest person is nearly 2 m tall.
- **a** Estimate the distance from the sea to the roof of the arch.
- **b** What can you tell from the photo about the rock structure?

4 Explain how the wave-cut platform between the headland at Rhossili and Worm's Head was formed.

5 Make a copy of the map of the Gower Peninsula (Figure 3.5).
- **a** Annotate it (add words such as arch, wave-cut platform and spit) to locate the features of erosion and deposition described in this section.
- **b** Add an arrow to Rhossili beach to show the direction of longshore drift.

6 Some parts of the coast described in this section are National Nature Reserves and should only be visited with the permission of the Nature Conservancy Council. Do you agree that this is a good use of these locations? Give reasons for your answer.

BEACH BUILDING

What happens to the rock which is broken from the Gower cliffs? Rough pieces are soon rounded off as they smash into each other. The smallest fragments become **sand** on the **beach**. In Rhossili Bay, waves (**swash**) from the south west carry grains of sand up the beach at an angle. The **backwash** returns straight down the beach because of gravity, taking some sand with it. Gradually a grain of sand will zig-zag its way along the beach. This is **longshore drift**. The movement continues until the coast changes direction, e.g. at a river mouth. At the north west tip of the Gower Peninsula, longshore drift has formed a finger of sand dunes at Whiteford: a **spit**. Between Rhossili and Whiteford, the sand spit has joined a small island, Burry Holms, to the rest of the peninsula again. This feature is a **tombolo**.

Cliff collapse: the disappearing coast of Holderness

Nowhere in the UK is land disappearing faster than on the Holderness coast. On average, 2 m a year is washed away, but in the first half of 1994 alone, the sea took 3 m. To the north resistant chalk forms vertical cliffs at Flamborough Head, a headland. Southwards to Spurn Point on the Humber estuary, the land is young and formed as a result of ice ages. Massive sheets of ice have covered this area several times and when melted they left behind soil and stones. Geologists can trace some of the stones to southern Scotland. The material, called **boulder clay**, now forms cliffs up to 15 m high. At high tide waves rapidly wash away the foot of the cliff to cut a **notch**. The unsupported boulder clay above will collapse onto the beach to be washed away by the sea. Clay shrinks and expands as the weather changes and cliff collapse is common after rain because wet clay is slippery and heavy. For hundreds of years, people in Holderness have accepted that the sea would get nearer until they had to abandon the village and build again further inland. Over the last 100 years though, people have come to expect that engineers could – and would – stop the sea. 10

Figure 3.7 The coastal defences at Mappleton

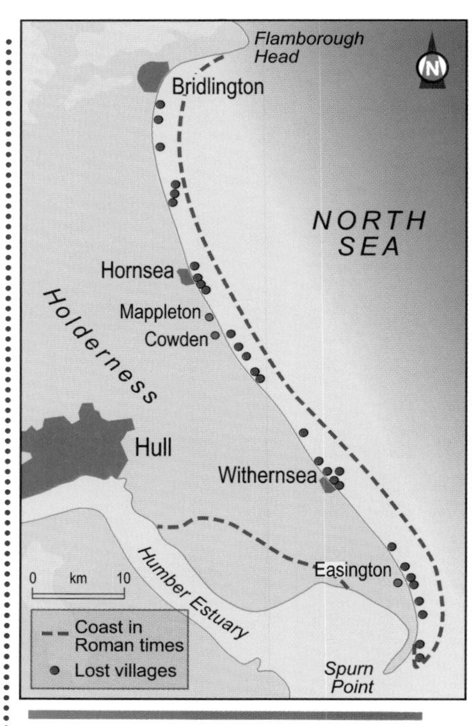

Figure 3.6 The Holderness coast

GOOD NEWS FOR MAPPLETON

Mappleton is a village that was established 200 years ago, then 1 km inland. Now the crumbling cliffs are just a few metres from the houses. If nothing had been done, the church would have fallen into the sea within 50 years. The government approved a £1.9 million scheme to save the village. Thirty per cent was paid for by the local council and the European Community also gave a grant. Thousands of tonnes of granite were shipped from Sweden in 1991 and unloaded onto the beach to make a protective wall at the foot of the cliffs. Two lines of boulders were also laid out to sea. These form barriers, like **groynes** to trap sand and shingle as longshore drift carries this material along the coast. With the beach expanded now, waves are more likely to break on the sand. Any waves which reach the top of the beach, crash against the granite rather than the cliff. To the north and south of Mappleton, the cliff face is dark brown but at Mappleton the grass is growing on it. The scheme was so successful that large numbers of sightseers come to visit and more than £7000 has been spent on a viewing area and car park! 10

1. Explain why the erosion of the Holderness coast is greatest **a** during north east gales; **b** at high tide.
2. Look at Figure 3.6.
   a How far has the coast receded since Roman times?
   b How many villages have been lost?
3. What has happened to the coastline inside the Humber estuary and how can this be explained?

BAD NEWS FOR COWDEN

Mappleton's success is not good news for Cowden, just 2 km along the coast. Most of the eroded boulder clay is fine material which is washed out to sea. Longshore drift only carries a small amount of sand along the Holderness coast. If more of this is trapped at Mappleton, there is less beach and more erosion at Cowden.

The scenic coastal road, Garthend Lane, had to be closed in 1994 after a crack 8 m long appeared. The road led to Sue Earle's farm, which is falling into the sea. Water supplies to the dairy were cut off when part of the cliff collapsed, breaking the pipe. Now the electricity supply is threatened as the cliff edge gets closer to the poles carrying the cables. She hopes to have one more winter in the farmhouse before it goes. She blames the coastal defence work at Mappleton and would like compensation from the council or government (Figure 3.8).

Figure 3.8 Farmer Sue Earle and her cat, Thomas, on the cliff edge, 1994

UNEASE AT EASINGTON

Along the coast at Easington, British Gas and BP have built terminals where the pipeline from the North Sea gas rigs comes ashore. The cliffs are now dangerously close and local people want a 1.6 km stretch of coast protecting with a rock barrier. This would safeguard the gas terminals and the village but it would cost £7 million. In 1994, the government decided it would only pay for the 1 km in front of the gas terminals to be protected. Unless the decision is changed, the 700 residents of Easington believe their homes, altogether worth about £15 million, as well as their pubs, shops and church will be destroyed.

Figure 3.9 A gas terminal at Easington, only a few metres from the cliff top

4 **a** Why is the cliff at Mappleton green?
b Why is it brown elsewhere?

5 Look at Figure 3.8. Estimate how many metres the cliff edge was from the dairy when the photo was taken.

6 In 1993, the Minister of Agriculture said, *'Protecting large swathes of rural coastline is no longer economically or environmentally justified. Trying to tame the action of waves and storms in one area often leads to damage elsewhere. Natural processes should only be disrupted where life or important man-made assets are at risk.'* In view of this should farmer Sue Earle at Cowden be paid compensation? Why?

7 Dr John Pethick from Hull University believes *'whole towns should be moved many miles inland behind new coastal defences over the next 100 years.'* If global warming leads to sea-level rising, erosion and flooding will increase. Forty per cent of the UK's industries are in coastal areas. Use an atlas to identify UK areas which could be lost to the sea. How will life in Britain be changed if nothing is done? Where should have priority for coastal defence schemes and where should 'managed retreat' be the policy?

TEMPERATURE AND RAINFALL IN THE UNITED KINGDOM

In the United Kingdom, we frequently talk about the **weather**, and it is often the first topic of conversation when two people meet. This is because our weather is so changeable from one day to the next.

The two terms, weather and **climate**, have quite different meanings. The weather is what is happening in the atmosphere at any particular time and refers to the temperature, wind, cloud cover and **precipitation** (rain, drizzle, frost, snow, hail, sleet, dew etc). It is the temperature and rainfall figures which are normally used to describe the weather. The climate of a place tells you the typical weather conditions which are likely to be experienced throughout the different seasons of the year. In the UK, the climate is described as equable, which means that it does not vary greatly from season to season.

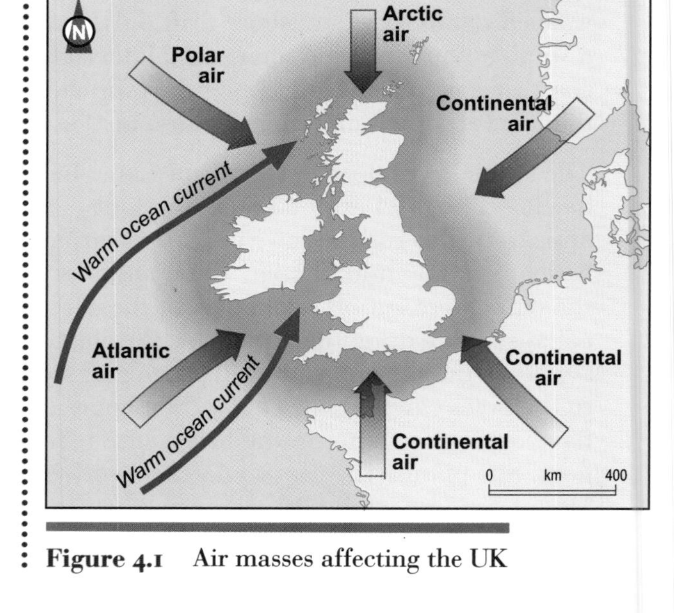

Figure 4.1 Air masses affecting the UK

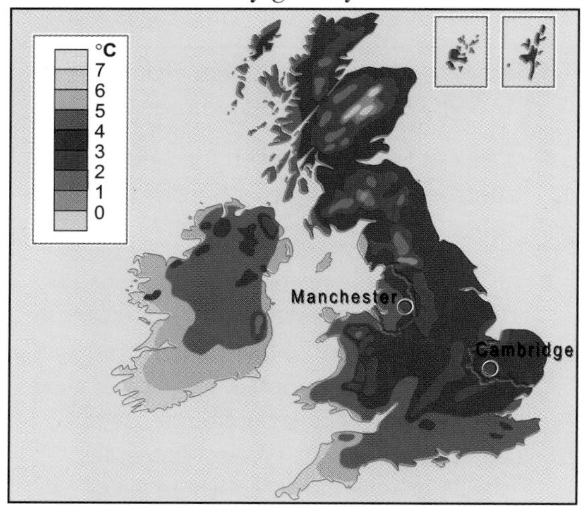

Figure 4.2 January temperatures in the UK

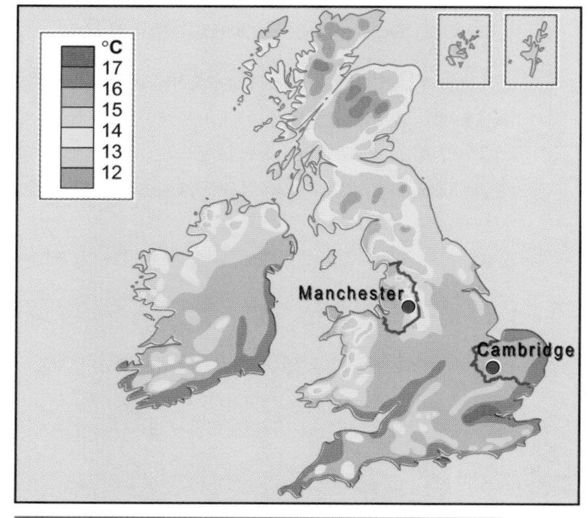

Figure 4.3 July temperatures in the UK

AIR MASSES AND THE SEASONS

In the UK, the climate is not the same all year. In the winter, it is colder and a little wetter than in the summer. This is because all the weather systems of the earth move north in our summer and south in our winter. In the summer, the UK has more **air masses** from the south over it and, in the winter, more air masses from the north.

An air mass is a very large amount of air which moves around the surface of the earth. Each air mass is different in temperature and the amount of moisture it is holding. Air masses from over the sea, are usually full of moisture, whereas those from over a large area of land, are usually dry. Air masses from near the equator, are warm and, from near one of the poles, are cold. The type of air mass over a place influences the weather experienced there.

Lots of different air masses pass over the UK and this causes the weather to vary a great deal.

1 Explain the difference between weather and climate.

2 Study the section on air masses.
   - **a** Make a copy of Figure 4.1 and shade in all the air mass arrows showing warm air flows in red and cold ones in blue. Add a 'W' to those arrows which will bring wet air and a 'D' to those which will bring dry air.
   - **b** From which part of the world have the air masses come which bring, i) hot dry weather in summer? ii) cold dry weather in winter?
   - **c** The air mass from the South West is the most common over the UK. What weather is it likely to bring?

WHAT AFFECTS THE TEMPERATURE?

The temperature of a place is affected by three main factors: **altitude** (height above sea-level), the type of air mass over the place at the time, and **latitude** (distance from the equator). It is colder as you go up hill (Figure 4.5). The amount of decrease in temperature, or **lapse rate**, is about 1°C for every 150 m. The highest land in the UK is not very high relatively, so this effect is limited.

THE HYDROLOGICAL CYCLE

Figure 4.4 shows the earth's hydrological or water cycle. It is called a cycle because water moves continuously within it, i.e. there is no beginning or end. Some of the water is in liquid form, some is invisible gas, and some solid ice. The width of the arrows shows roughly how much water is involved in each part of the cycle.

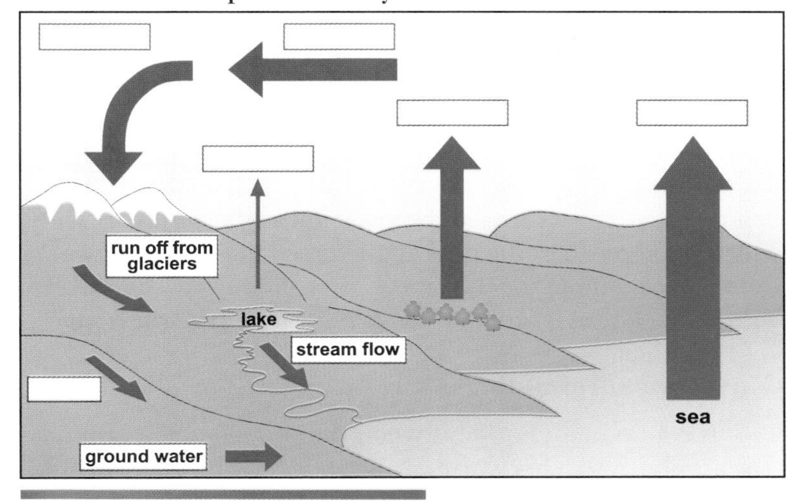

Figure 4.4 The hydrological cycle

Most **evaporation** takes place when the sun's energy warms the water in the oceans, changing some of it into an invisible gas called water vapour, held in the atmosphere. Water also evaporates from rivers, lakes, reservoirs, marshes and soil into the atmosphere. Plants draw up water from the soil and pass it into the atmosphere; this is known as **transpiration**. **Evapotranspiration** describes both processes which move water into the atmosphere.

Water vapour moves in the atmosphere. If it cools as it moves, it **condenses** (changes from a gas to a liquid) into visible minute water droplets – if it is very cold, ice crystals form. These droplets and crystals are seen as clouds and under certain conditions, become so large and heavy that they fall to the earth's surface as precipitation.

If precipitation falls on land, it may be evaporated or transpired again; it may return to the sea along rivers; or it may **infiltrate** (soak into) the soil and rocks and seep downhill until it reaches a river or the sea.

Figure 4.5 Snow-capped mountains and sunny beach

3 How many degrees colder than at sea-level will it be at the following places on a typical day?
- **a** Summit of Mount Snowdon (1085 m).
- **b** Summit of Ben Nevis (1344 m).
- **c** London (45 m).
- **d** Belfast (75 m).

4 Make your own copy of Figure 4.4, adding the following labels – each term may be used more than once. Evaporation; transpiration; precipitation; condensation; infiltration.

5 Study Figures 4.2 and 4.3 on page 14.
- **a** Is the east side of the UK warmer or colder than the west side in January? Why?
- **b** Is the southern part of the UK warmer or colder than the nothern part in July? Why?

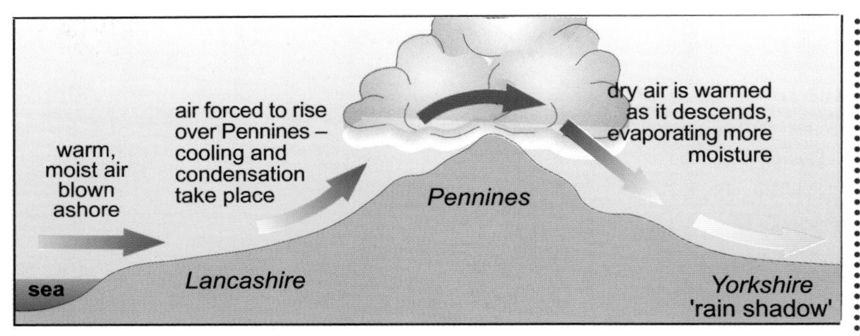

Figure 4.6 Relief rainfall over the Pennines

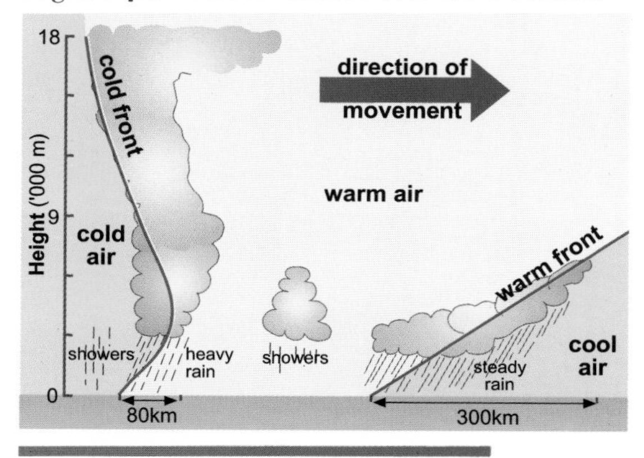

Figure 4.7 Cross-section through a depression

6 Which type of rainfall is likely to occur,
- **a** on a hot summer's day;
- **b** at the top of a range of hills;
- **c** by the coast on a cloudy day?

7 Explain what is meant by a dry 'rain shadow' area. You may find it useful to draw a labelled diagram similar to the one in Figure 4.6.

8 Study Figure 4.7 and answer these questions.
- **a** What will be the first thing visible in the atmosphere as a depression approaches?
- **b** What type of rain will be the first to fall?
- **c** Will the temperature become warmer or colder as the warm front passes overhead?
- **d** What type of rain falls as the cold front passes overhead?
- **e** Approximately how many kilometres wide is a depression?

9 Study rainfall and relief maps of the UK using an atlas. Describe the link between the two maps.

TYPES OF RAINFALL

When air in the atmosphere is forced to rise, it cools and it might rain. There are three different reasons why air may be forced to rise in the atmosphere and therefore three different types of rainfall called **frontal**, **relief** and **convectional**

Relief rainfall

As air rises over a range of hills or mountains, it is cooled and the water vapour within it condenses into droplets of liquid, which we see as clouds. As these droplets increase in number and size, they become heavy and fall as rain (Figure 4.6). In general the higher you go, the wetter the climate.

Frontal or depression rainfall

Many depressions cross our islands and they are more common in winter than in summer. A depression forms when a warm, moist air mass from the south meets a colder, drier air mass from the north. Figure 4.7 shows a cross-section of a depression and the weather at different places as the depression passes overhead. Rain occurs as the warm air, which is lighter than the cold air, is forced to rise at the two fronts. It rises more quickly at the steep cold front and the rain here is much heavier than at the gently sloping warm front.

Convectional rainfall

This is common on hot days when the sun heats the ground and air above it. This warm air becomes lighter and rises. It is then replaced by cool air, which is also warmed and rises. This movement is called a **convection current**. As the air rises, it cools and any moisture present in it condenses into droplets. As the air rises further, more droplets form, together becoming large enough to fall as rain. This type of rain is usually very heavy and often accompanied by thunderstorms. It does not usually last for long, as the rain cools down the surface, so stopping the convection current.

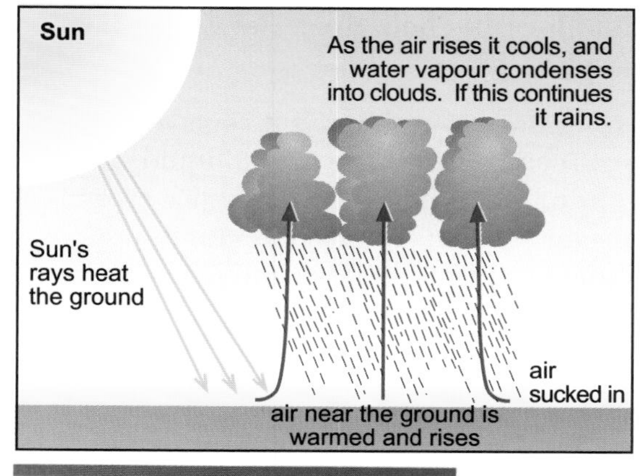

Figure 4.8 Convectional rainfall

Variations in temperature and rainfall: a case study of the North West and East Anglia

The UK is a small country and the climate varies only slightly from one area to another, but there are differences.

THE NORTH WEST OF ENGLAND

In the North West, the climate is affected greatly by the prevailing winds (the most common ones) which are from the south west. This means that they cross a warm tropical ocean current called the North Atlantic Drift (see Figure 4.1) before reaching the region and tend to make the region warmer than it might be, especially in winter. These winds are also very moist and bring rain throughout the year. It is wettest in the upland areas and the driest parts of the region are in the south of Cheshire. In this area the air has already lost most of its moisture as rain on the Welsh mountains and we say it is in the **rain shadow** of these mountains.

EAST ANGLIA

East Anglia experiences some extreme weather, mainly because it is close to the continent of Europe and furthest from the large Atlantic Ocean and its moderating effects.

This region is very dry because the prevailing south-westerly winds are dry, having crossed large areas of land already. The less frequent winds from the east bring cold air from the continent in winter and with it severe frosts and snow.

Month	J	F	M	A	M	J	J	A	S	O	N	D
MANCHESTER (NORTH WEST)												
Temperature (°C)	4	4	6	8	11	14	16	15	13	11	7	5
Rainfall (mm)	67	52	52	50	60	63	78	83	76	69	77	79
Total hours of bright sunshine	42	62	107	140	185	189	160	157	123	96	57	41
CAMBRIDGE (EAST ANGLIA)												
Temperature (°C)	3	4	6	8	12	15	17	16	13	10	7	4
Rainfall (mm)	45	30	30	45	45	35	60	45	50	45	40	35
Total hours of bright sunshine	50	65	118	149	189	204	189	180	138	102	57	40

Figure 4.9 Climate figures for Manchester and Cambridge

Region	North West England	East Anglia
Season of most rainfall		
Total rainfall		
Main types of rainfall		
Temperature of coldest month		
Temperature of hottest month		
Total number of hours of bright sunshine		

Figure 4.10 Climate contrasts between the North West and East Anglia

1. Draw two climate graphs using Figure 4.9 to compare the climates of the North West and East Anglia.
2. Using the completed climate graphs, answer the following questions on the regions.
   - **a** Which has the most rainfall?
   - **b** Which has the hottest summers?
   - **c** Which has the coldest winters?
   - **d** Which type of rainfall is likely in the summer in East Anglia? Why?
   - **e** Which region has the most hours of bright sunshine?
   - **f** Why are frosts rare in the North West?
3. Copy and complete Figure 4.10 and write two sentences comparing the climate of these two regions. You should use the following phrases: cold winters; mild winters; hot summers; cool summers; wet climate; dry climate; sunny climate.
4. The climate of both regions can cause problems for the farmers. What problems do you think might be caused?

For these questions use Figure 5.1.

1 Make a list of ecosystem **inputs** (which come from outside) and then a list of **outputs**.
2 Which of the influences shown in the diagram are due to humans?
3 Write down three other ways in which humans influence ecosystems which are not described in the diagram.

WHAT IS AN ECOSYSTEM?

An ecosystem is an area in which the climate, soil and other elements of the environment work together to produce a particular pattern of plant and animal life. An ecosystem can be very small, such as a goldfish bowl, or very large – the whole of Highland Scotland for example.

Figure 5.1 summarises the main influences on an ecosystem. In the UK the influence of humans is particularly great: there are few areas where the natural ecosystem has not been altered by either farmers or developers.

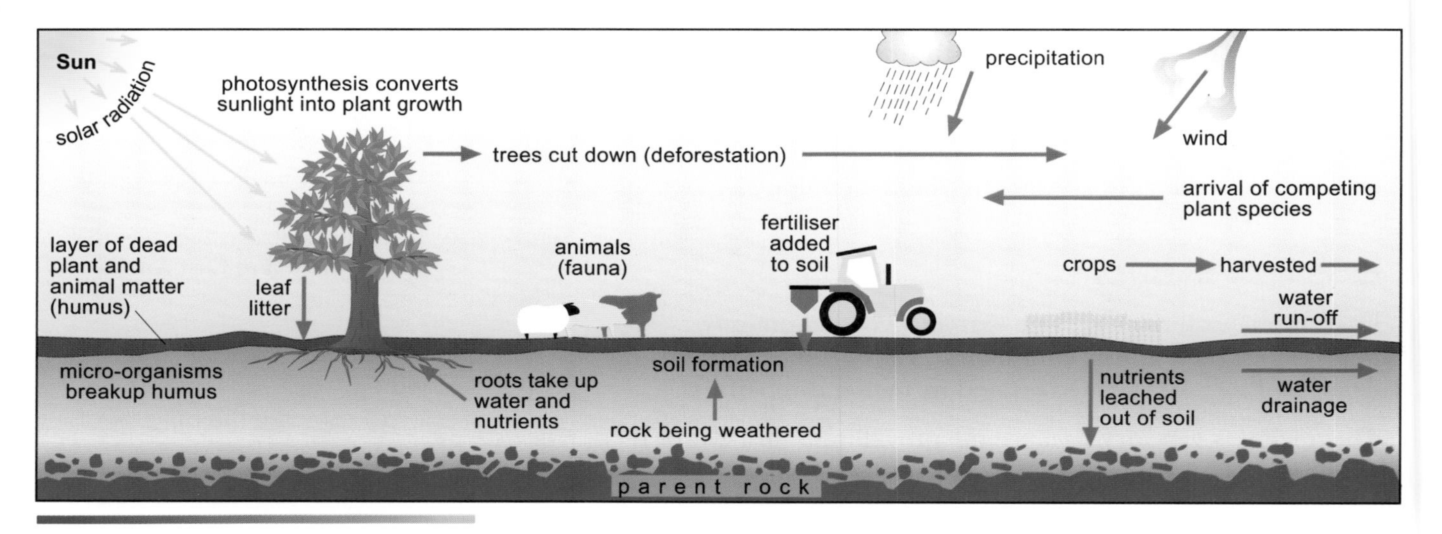

Figure 5.1 Elements of an ecosystem

Ecosystems: a case study of heather moorland, Highlands of Scotland

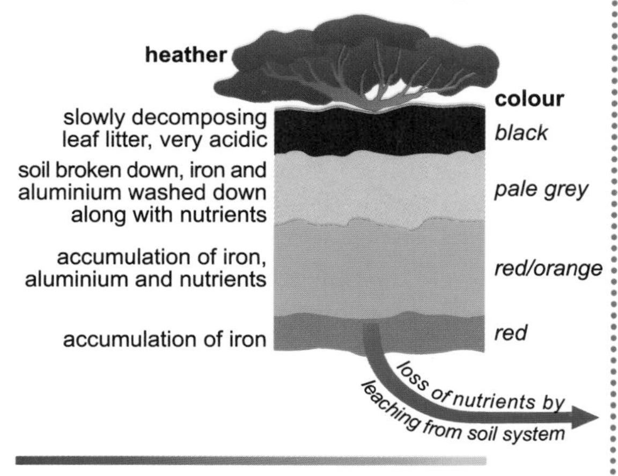

Figure 5.2 Soil profile under heather

Figure 5.3 Heather moorland in Scotland

Figures 5.3 and 5.5 show where heather moorland is found and what it is like. This is the main ecosystem on land above 200 m, covering much of Wales, the Pennines, moors in the south west, and the Antrim Hills in Northern Ireland. The largest area, however, is in Highland Scotland.

WHY IS HEATHER MOORLAND FOUND WHERE IT IS?

Soil

Heather grows on thin, acid, infertile soils where other plants cannot grow. Heather has adapted to tolerate such soil.

Figure 5.5 shows that most of the heather moorland areas are uplands. These regions often have poor soils – a result of rock type, cold weather and heavy rain. The lower areas, more accessible to farmers, with a milder climate, have been converted into grassland for grazing cattle.

Figures 5.2 and 5.4 show the profile of a typical soil found underneath heather. It is called a **podsol**, and is one of the poorest types of soil found in the UK. Rotting pieces of dead heather make the soil very acidic and it is almost impossible for other plants to grow with the heather. It also reduces the number of earthworms, which are useful at breaking up the soil, releasing minerals for use by plants, and so the lack of them reduces soil fertility even more.

Human interference

Much of the area occupied by heather today was originally wooded. During Neolithic times (3000–2000 BC) the trees were felled which left the soil open to the impact of rain. **Leaching** occurred and nutrients in the topsoil were washed to lower layers, out of reach of the plant roots.

Climate

Heather would have been the natural vegetation in some places in Scotland even before human interference: the very exposed areas near the coast, where strong winds and sandy soil deter other species, and the wettest parts of the western highlands where soil leaching is severe.

MOORLAND SUCCESSION

If the heather moorland is not burned or grazed, it soon begins to change. Towards the end of the heather life cycle the plants collapse and this allows other species to invade the area. This is known as **plant succession**. At first the moorland turns into scrub (low bushes) and eventually to oak woodland.

Figure 5.4 A podsol. Notice the dull colour of the layer beneath the soil. This has suffered from leaching

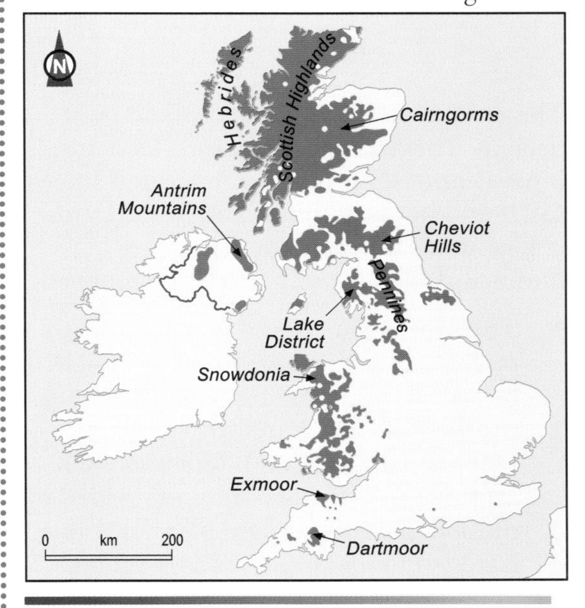

Figure 5.5 Distribution of heather moorland in the UK

MOORLAND MANAGEMENT

For many years plant succession on the moors was prevented by burning. Burning the heather in a controlled way enables new heather to grow and kills off rival species – heather can survive burning better than other species. The burning takes place towards the end of the building phase, before the plant becomes too **woody**. In Scotland small patches of about 1 ha are burnt every year: this leaves enough heather around the burnt patch to provide cover for grouse. The old plants are destroyed by the burning but buds just below the surface survive.

Heather moorland has been managed in this way because it has been used for grazing hill sheep. Large areas are also used for grouse-shooting and deer-hunting.

Conservationists are keen to maintain heather moorlands because of the wide variety of wildlife they support. Rare birds which need heather moorland include merlins, hen harriers, and grouse. Mountain hare and red deer are two important animal species.

LOSS OF HEATHER MOORLAND

The total area of heather moorland is in decline. The Scottish Highlands have lost 8 per cent of their heather moorland since 1970 and in places like Exmoor the figure is four times this amount. There are a number of reasons why this has happened.

- The heather moorland is being *turned into grassland*, which provides much better food for grazing sheep. First the heather is burned and the soils ploughed and drained. Minerals such as nitrogen and potassium are added to the soil, and grasses are planted. Lime is added to make the soil less acidic.

4 Give two reasons why heather is found mainly in upland areas.

5 Write down three features of the soil found under heather moorland.

6 What is plant succession and how does it work?

7 Describe the changes which take place to the plant community shown in Figure 5.7.

8 Why do some people want to preserve heather moorland?

9 Why is the area of heather moorland gradually declining?

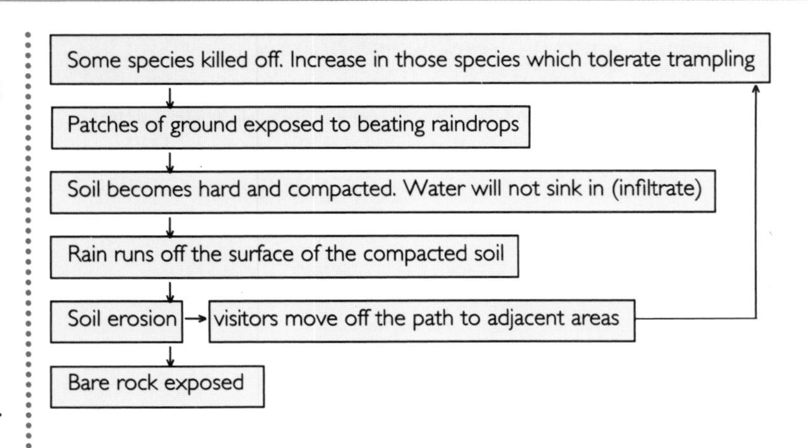

Figure 5.6 The impact of trampling on moorland

- *Lack of moorland management*, allowing it to change to scrub. In some areas the farmers have given up using the moors for grazing and have stopped burning the heather. This has allowed bracken to invade. Figure 5.7 shows the changes which took place on a survey site 30 years after burning. Bracken is a problem because it causes ill-health in animals and people.
- *Footpath erosion.* The Scottish Highlands are an important tourist area. Figure 5.6 shows some of the effects of soil erosion caused by people trampling on the moors.
- *Afforestation.* Since the end of the 1914–18 war the Forestry Commission has been encouraging landowners to plant trees on their own land. Tax advantages have been provided to make this attractive. Because the soils in heather moorland are poor, the trees which have been planted have tended to be those which could tolerate these poor soils, e.g. conifers. There has been criticism of this policy because regular blocks of trees can look odd in the landscape, and the plant and animal life associated with heather moorland is destroyed.

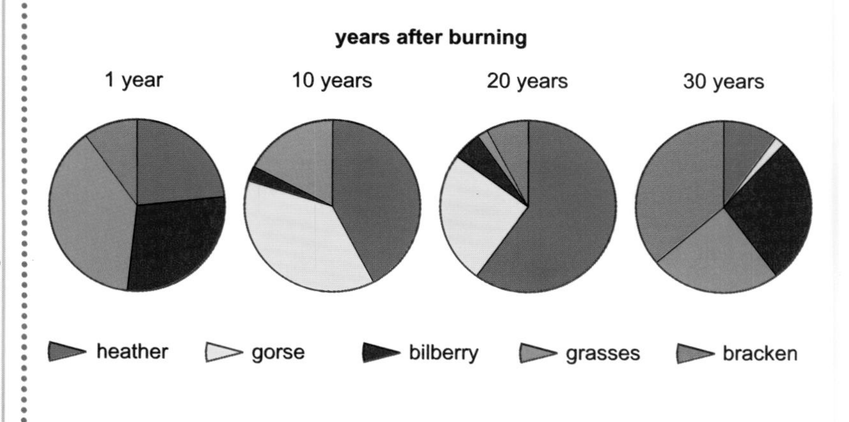

Figure 5.7 Changes in a moorland community over time

6 population

POPULATION DISTRIBUTION: THIS IS WHERE I LIVE

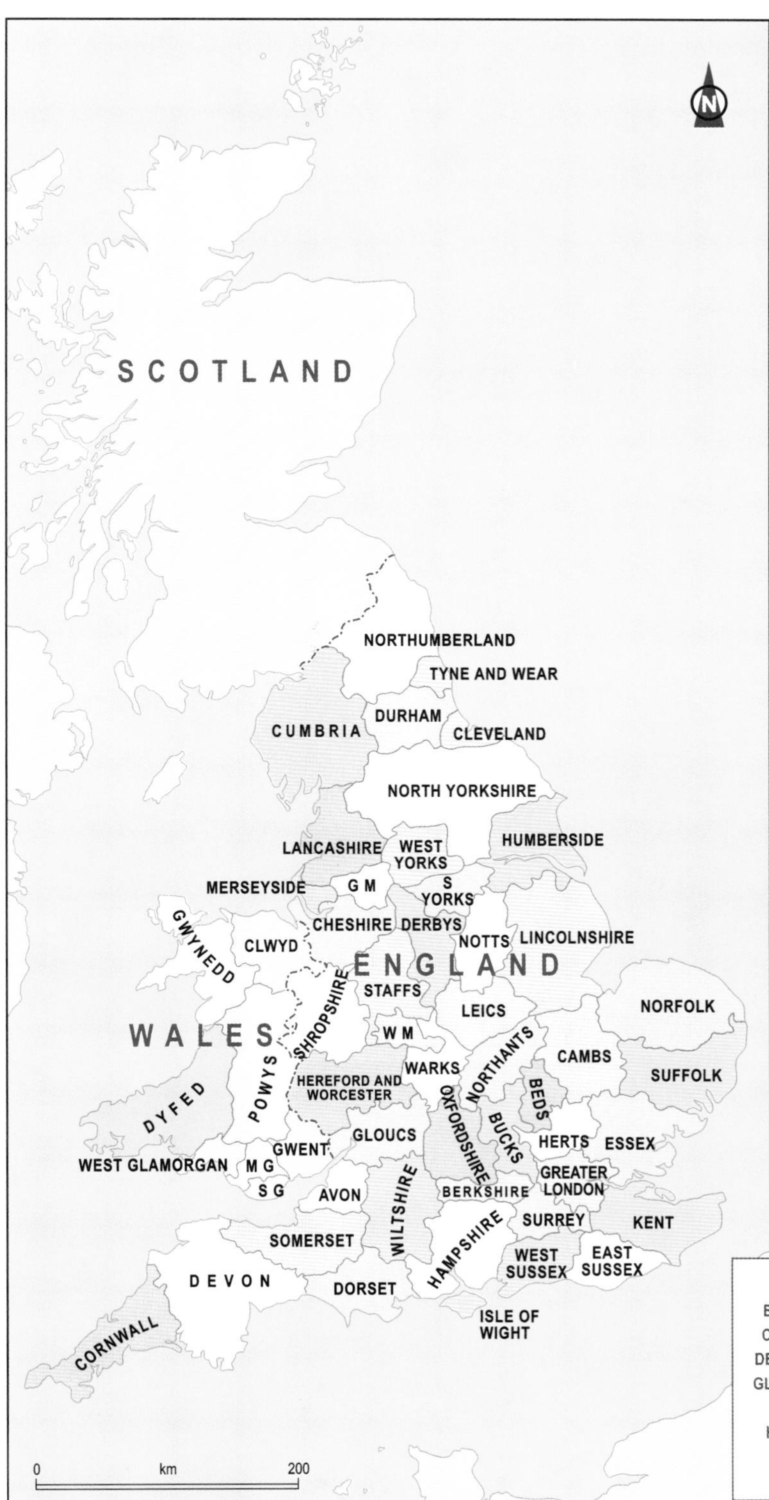

BEDS	BEDFORDSHIRE	NORTHANTS	NORTHAMPTONSHIRE
BUCKS	BUCKINGHAMSHIRE	NOTTS	NOTTINGHAMSHIRE
CAMBS	CAMBRIDGESHIRE	S G	SOUTH GLAMORGAN
DERBYS	DERBYSHIRE	STAFFS	STAFFORDSHIRE
GLOUCS	GLOUCESTERSHIRE	S YORKS	SOUTH YORKSHIRE
G M	GREATER MANCHESTER	WARKS	WARWICKSHIRE
HERTS	HERTFORDSHIRE	W M	WEST MIDLANDS
LEICS	LEICESTERSHIRE	WEST YORKS	WEST YORKSHIRE
M G	MID GLAMORGAN		

Figure 6.1 County boundaries in England and Wales

Have you ever run the 100 m race? Imagine that distance as the side of a square. Imagine that your home is at the centre of that square. Now see if you can work out how many people live in that area around your home. Don't forget yourself and your own family!

You are starting to think about the **density** of population. This means the number of people in an area. It is usually measured as persons per hectare. Remember the square with your home in the middle? That square is one hectare. If ten people live in your square, the population is ten persons per hectare. Do you think that is **dense** (crowded) or **sparse** (spread out)?

The area around your home may have a very different population density to the rest of your region. If you live in a town, there will be parts where very few people live, such as areas of factories and the centre of the town may only house pub landlords and some people living above the shops. There are also parks, cemeteries and all the land used for roads, car parks and traffic islands. Can you think of other parts of your region with low population density?

You should not be surprised if the population density of your 'square' seems high. All these other land uses account for the average for your region. For the whole of England and Wales, there are only 3.3 persons per hectare.

Do you think the population of your county has increased or decreased during your lifetime? For each county in England and Wales, you can find the answer on Figure 6.2. It shows the annual percentage rate of change. A decrease of 1.00 would mean that for each year and for every 100 people in the county, there would be 99 people one year later. That might not seem much but percentage figures can be misleading. For example, the 1991 census showed the number of people in Tyne and Wear reducing by 0.48 per cent a year. That, however, means there were 44 850 fewer people than ten years before!

Other counties in the Tyne and Wear region, e.g. Northumberland, are seeing their populations rise. Most of this change is due to people moving out of the area. As people get older, many prefer to live in a small rather than a large place. To see what was happening 30 years ago look at Figure 6.3.

1 Each person should write their initials and the population density of the hectare containing their home on the board.
   a Who lives in the most densely populated area?
   b Who lives in a sparsely populated area?

2 a Would you expect a high rise flat to have a high population density?
   b Would you expect a farm to have a low population density?

3 Work out the average population density for the class. (Add up the numbers on the board and divide by the number of pupils.) How does it compare with the average for England and Wales?

4 a Make a copy of the county boundaries in your region from Figure 6.1. Write the title, 'Population Density in 1991'. With one coloured pencil colour in the counties with low population densities lightly and the higher densities progressively darker. Use Figure 6.5. Don't forget your key.
   b On your map, mark * where you live.
   c How does your 1991 map compare with the 1981 map in Figure 6.4?

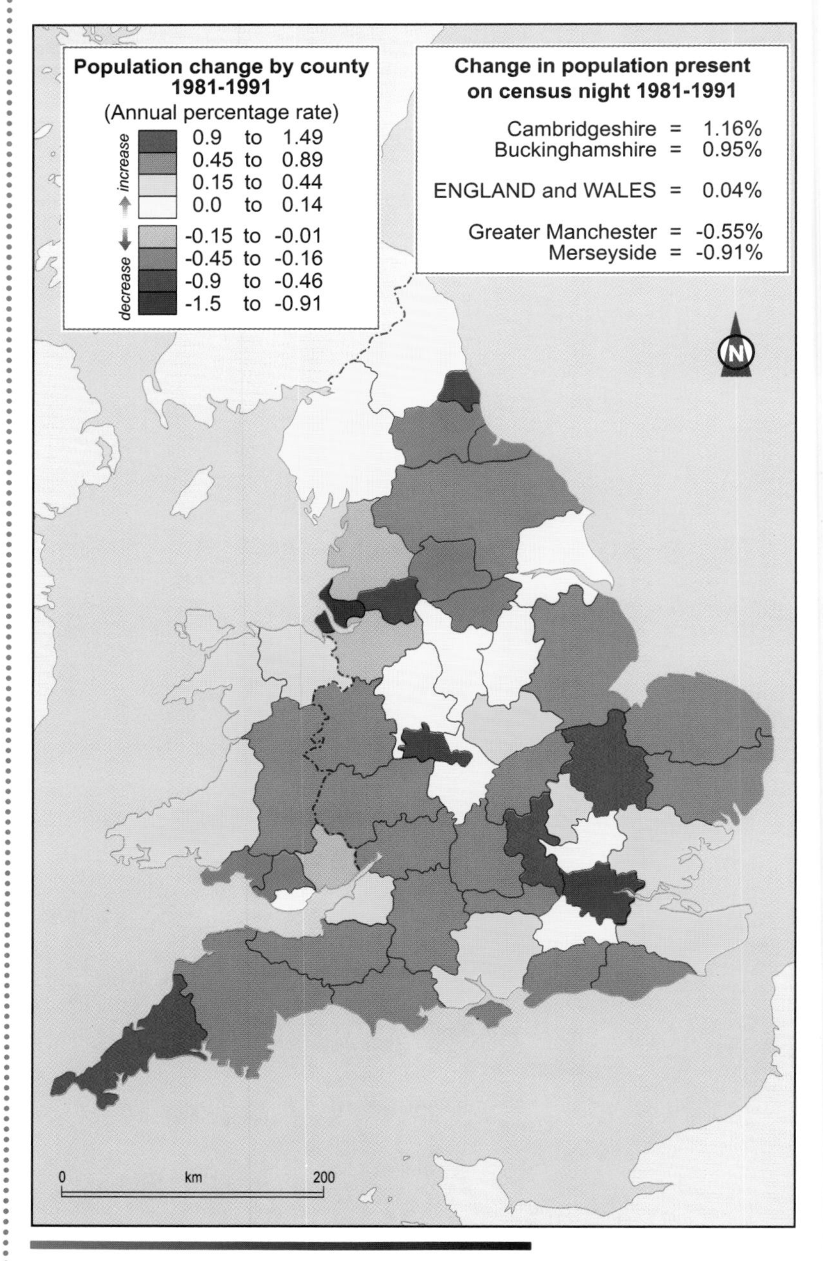

Figure 6.2 Population change 1981–1991

5 a Looking at Figure 6.2, which counties in your region appear to have gained population as people have moved out of older industrial areas?
   b Suggest reasons why some people have moved from older industrial areas to one of these counties.

6 Either do a class survey, or for homework do a survey in your neighbourhood to find out who has moved into your county during your lifetime.

7 Do you think living in a small place is better than living in a large settlement? What are your reasons?

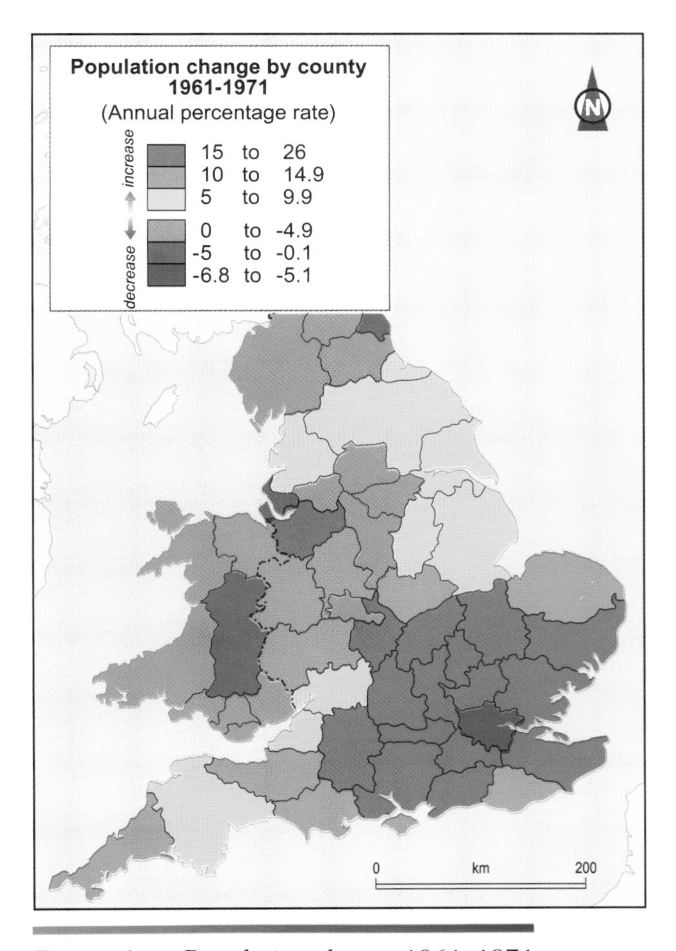

Figure 6.3 Population change 1961–1971

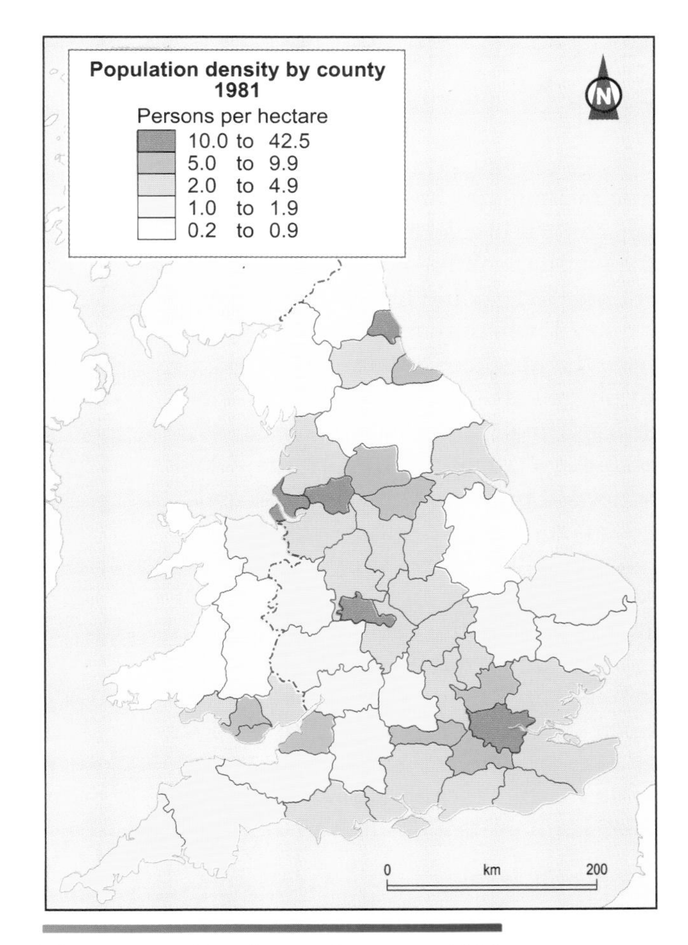

Figure 6.4 Population density in 1981

County	Population density	County	Population density	County	Population density
Avon	7.0	Hampshire	4.1	South Yorkshire	8.1
Bedfordshire	4.2	Hereford and Worcester	1.7	Staffordshire	3.8
Berkshire	5.8	Hertfordshire	6.0	Suffolk	1.7
Buckingham	3.4	Humberside	2.4	Surrey	6.1
Cambridge	1.9	Isle of Wight	3.3	Tyne and Wear	20.4
Cheshire	4.1	Kent	4.0	Warwickshire	2.4
Cleveland	9.2	Lancashire	4.5	West Midlands	28.4
Cornwall and Isles of Scilly	1.3	Leicestershire	3.4	West Sussex	3.6
Cumbria	0.7	Lincolnshire	1.0	West Yorkshire	9.9
Derbyshire	3.5	Merseyside	21.4	Wiltshire	1.6
Devon	1.5	Norfolk	1.4	Clwyd	1.7
Dorset	2.4	Northampton	2.4	Dyfed	0.6
Durham	2.4	Northumberland	0.6	Gwent	3.2
East Sussex	3.8	North Yorkshire	0.8	Gwynedd	0.6
Essex	4.2	Nottingham	4.6	Mid Glamorgan	5.2
Gloucester	2.0	Oxfordshire	2.1	Powys	0.2
Greater London	42.3	Shropshire	1.2	South Glamorgan	9.4
Greater Manchester	19.4	Somerset	1.3	West Glamorgan	4.4

Figure 6.5 Population density of counties in 1991, persons per hectare

People in a rural area: a case study of the Welsh Borderlands

Imagine you are the Planning Officer for the council in a large rural area. This means that you have to recommend where builders should be allowed to put new houses, where roads should be improved and where money should be spent on schools, health centres and sports facilities. The population of the area is changing. For more than 100 years, farms have needed fewer workers as more and bigger machines have taken over. There is no longer a village blacksmith. Many of the activities which used to happen locally on a small scale, like brewing beer, are now done on a large scale far away. This is known as using **economies of scale**. It's cheaper! The cost of transport for the extra distances is low with the use of big lorries and fast roads. The population of the remoter rural areas continues to decline.

Young people leaving school in this area know there are more jobs in the towns than in the countryside. They are already used to the towns. That is where the secondary schools are because there are just not enough young people living in a village to fill a secondary school there. So every day, many pupils from villages make the journey into town for lessons. Here too, are the bright lights with places to meet people and things to do in the evenings.

Figure 6.7 Traditional style modern house in Luston

Figure 6.6 Old and new houses in Luston

As the Planning Officer, you do not, of course, have as much money to spend as you would like and it is tempting to spend it where the most people are. A new youth club would serve more young people in the town than in one of the villages. With more services, such as youth clubs, and more job opportunities in the towns, many of the young people brought up in villages will decide to move to a town when they leave home. Most of the new houses are being built in the towns too.

As Planning Officer, you allow some new developments in villages. Larger villages, which already have some facilities, and especially those close to towns may grow. You will need to consider whether new buildings will spoil the character of the village, whether high quality farmland will be built on and whether the roads can cope with the extra traffic. It may all be decided by something as simple as the capacity of the village's sewage works!

1 People from a village write to you, as the Planning Officer, suggesting that the money being spent on towns should be used in the villages instead. Do you agree with them? Write down your reasons.

2 Look at the photographs in Figures 6.6 and 6.7.
   a How have the planners tried to blend old and new buildings?
   b How well have they succeeded?

3 Look at the Ordnance Survey extract in Figure 6.8.
   a How far does Nancy travel from Luston to school in Leominster?
   b Which road does she take?
   c What shape (form) is the village of Luston?
   d Suggest why it is this shape.

4 Most of the recent houses are in cul de sacs to the west of the main road. Use the Ordnance Survey map to suggest why the village has not grown eastwards.

5 a How many main roads ('A' class roads) meet up at Leominster?
   b Name three facilities shown in Leominster which are not found in Luston.
   c What is the map evidence that flooding has been a problem in north Leominster?

WELCOME TO LUSTON

Nancy Bray, a pupil at the Minster School in Leominster, Hereford and Worcester, studied her village of Luston. Find it in grid squares 4862 and 4863 in Figure 6.8. About 500 people live here, enough for a shop, a primary school, a Methodist chapel and a pub. The village shop sells almost everything and is the post office too. Nancy found out there used to be other shops – a greengrocer and a cobbler as well as a blacksmith and a wheelwright. The pub is called *The Balance* because many years ago, wool was weighed here before being taken to market.

In the last 40 years, more people have been able to afford cars. Luston is no longer thought of as isolated and Nancy found that most people considered it *'an attractive, unspoilt place to live'*. If it continues to grow, will it still be attractive and unspoilt? Nancy asked 13 people who had moved to Luston why they had chosen the village. Six said they were attracted by the village environment, all but four had moved in from outside the region and none worked in Luston.

In some villages, most new residents are retired and some houses are bought as holiday homes which may be empty for most of the time. Wealthy people from the cities can afford to pay more than most local families. To buy a house, a young person brought up in the village may have no choice but to move to the town. What is the effect of this on the village community?

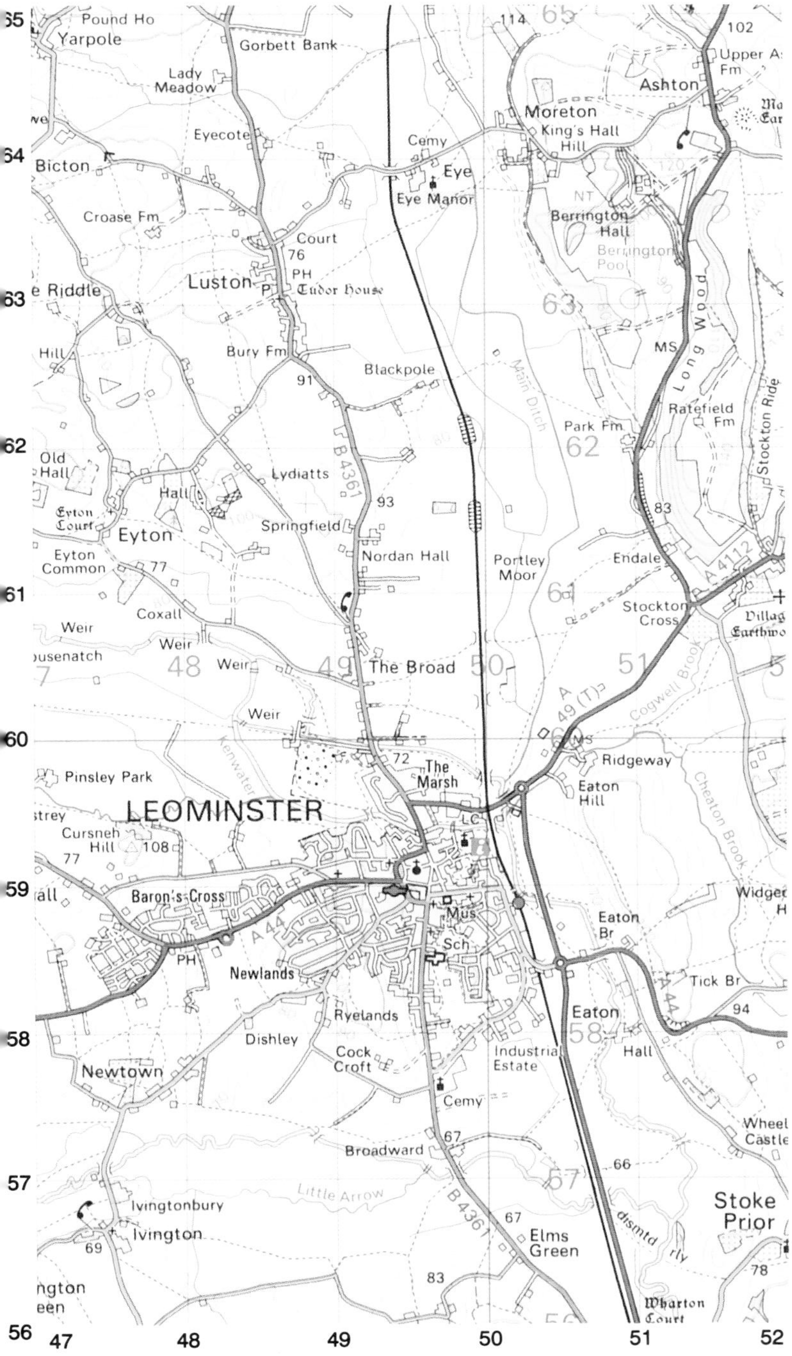

Figure 6.8 Ordnance Survey Landranger 149, scale 1:50 000 (2 cm = 1 km). © Crown Copyright

Urban population: a case study of London and the South East

1991 Census England

H form for Private Households

To the Head or Joint Heads or members of the Household aged 16 or over

...ase complete this form for all members of the household, ...luding children, and have it ready for collection on Monday 22nd April. Your census enumerator will call to collect it then or soon afterwards and will help you with the form if you have any difficulties. The enclosed leaflet explains why the Census is necessary and how the information is used.

Whereabouts on night of 21-22 April 1991

Please tick the appropriate box to indicate where the person was on the night of 21-22 April 1991.

At this address, out on night work or travelling to this address ☐ 0
Elsewhere in England, Scotland or Wales ☐ 1
Outside Great Britain ☐

Marital status

On the 21st April what is the person's marital status?
If separated but not divorced, please tick 'Married (first marriage)' or 'Re-married' as appropriate.
Please tick one box.

Single (never married) ☐ 1
Married (first marriage) ☐ 2
Re-married ☐ 3
Divorced (decree absolute) ☐ 4
Widowed ☐ 5

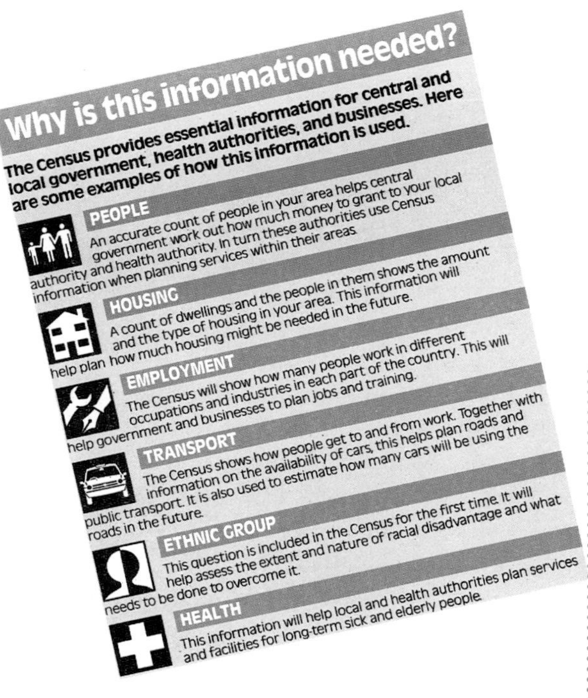

Why is this information needed?

The census provides essential information for central and local government, health authorities, and businesses. Here are some examples of how this information is used.

PEOPLE
An accurate count of people in your area helps central government work out how much money to grant to your local authority and health authority. In turn these authorities use Census information when planning services within their areas.

HOUSING
A count of dwellings and the people in them shows the amount and the type of housing in your area. This information will help plan how much housing might be needed in the future.

EMPLOYMENT
The Census will show how many people work in different occupations and industries in each part of the country. This will help government and businesses to plan jobs and training.

TRANSPORT
The Census shows how people get to and from work. Together with information on the availability of cars, this helps plan roads and public transport. It is also used to estimate how many cars will be using the roads in the future.

ETHNIC GROUP
This question is included in the Census for the first time. It will help assess the extent and nature of racial disadvantage and what needs to be done to overcome it.

HEALTH
This information will help local and health authorities plan services and facilities for long-term sick and elderly people.

Figure 6.9 The 1991 census

1. Why do you think the plans for a census in 1941 were abandoned?
2. Look at Figure 6.10.
   - **a** Name the London boroughs that have the highest percentage of households with one adult living alone.
   - **b** Describe which part of London they are in.
   - **c** Suggest why living in this part of London is attractive to young, single people.
3. Look at Figure 6.11.
   - **a** Describe the location of the London boroughs with the highest percentages of people in professional occupations.
   - **b** From Figure 6.11, suggest one factor which helps to give some of these areas an attractive environment.
   - **c** Which part of London has the fewest professional people?

On the night of Sunday 21 April 1991, every household in the UK had to fill in a **census** form. Every ten years since 1801 there has been a census. The only exception was 1941. The census asks many questions about who we are, our homes, jobs, qualifications, journeys to work and health. For the first time, in 1991 a question was included about our racial or ethnic group. Previously the census has only asked about country of birth. Many people can trace their family ancestry to other countries and may feel their roots are there, although they were born in the UK, e.g. many Afro-Caribbean families in Brixton, south London. 'Country of birth' does not always indicate someone's ethnic group. A large number of Indian-born people were shown to live in Surrey, many of them born to British Army families before India became independent.

The census, however, does more than count the rising population. For London though, the 1991 census showed the total population at 6 679 699. It had been almost 8 million 30 years earlier. However, the population of the South East region grew by 3.2 per cent between 1981 and 1991. This was due to two factors.

- **Natural increase.** This is the balance between the number of people born and the number dying. The fact that more people were born in the South East region than died was the most important reason for the population growth. It accounts for over 80 per cent of the increase since the previous census. In fact the South East had a remarkable 50 per cent of all the natural increase in the UK between 1981 and 1991, largely due to the high birth rate amongst ethnic minorities and the large number of young couples in the region.
- **Migration** to the region. In the past many people have moved from the South East to live in other regions, especially East Anglia and the South West. However, since 1981, more people have moved into the region than left it. Mainly they have come from the South West, the North West and the Midlands.

Figure 6.10 Households with one adult living alone

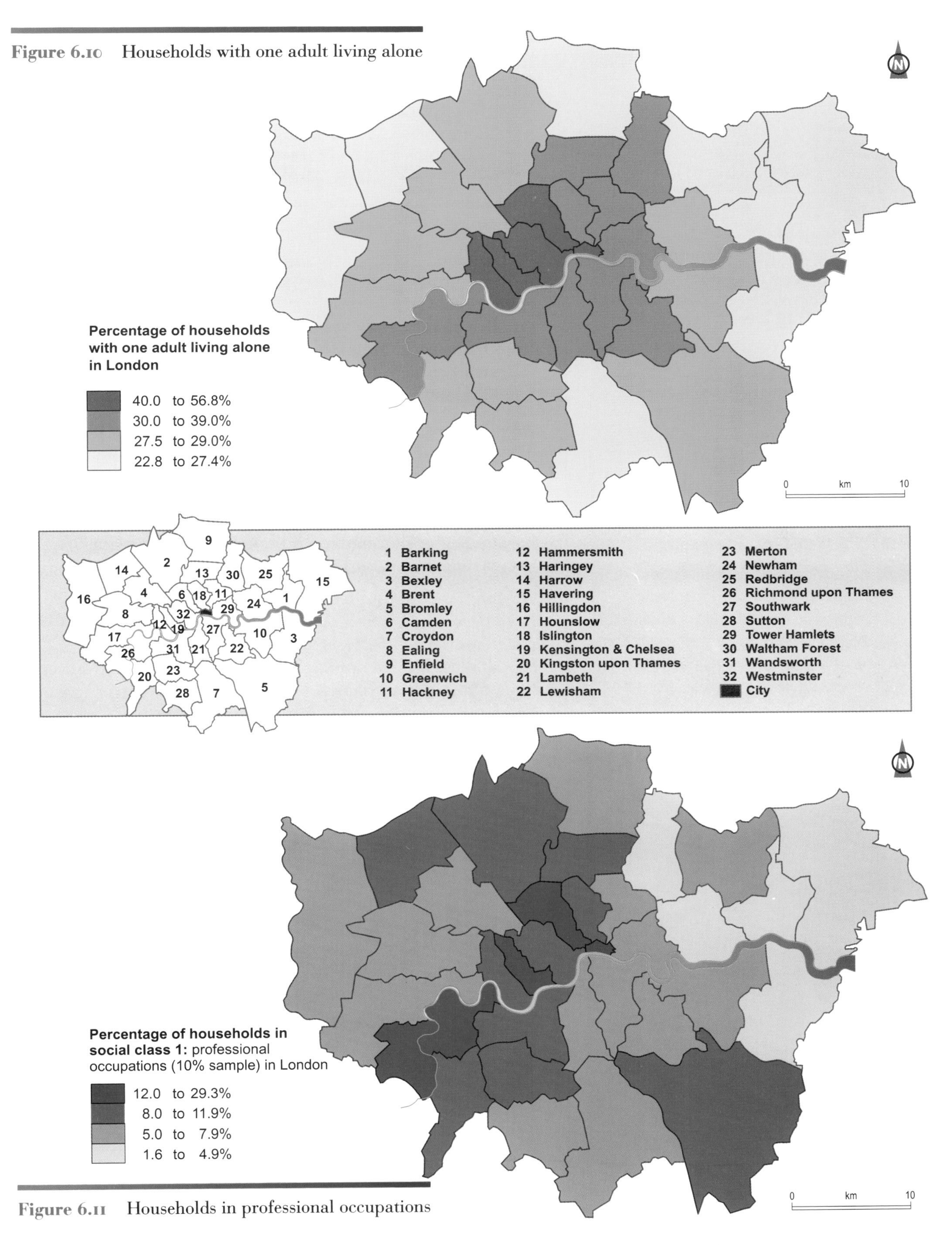

Figure 6.11 Households in professional occupations

4 Suggest a reason why houses may cost less as the distance from London increases.

5 Explain what is meant by *'the rural areas have a more attractive environment'*.

6 The rural regions around Basingstoke, Bedford and Basildon are three areas whose populations have increased as people have moved out from London. However, many people still work in London and commute daily. Find one of these towns in your atlas.
   a Measure the distance to central London from the town you have chosen.
   b Assuming an average speed of 50 km per hour, work out the travelling time to work.
   c If the commuter is at work from 9 am to 5 pm, write down a possible day's timetable from getting up to arriving home from work.
   d In your opinion, is this acceptable? What is the maximum travelling time you consider reasonable? How might commuting in the South East be affected by fare rises, transport improvements, job relocations and gentrification?

So, why did London's population fall? Since the beginning of this century there has been a wave of growth rippling out from London, like a wave created when a stone is thrown into a pond. In the 1930s, the area of fastest growth was the suburbs of London. In the 1960s, many people moved out to a ring of new towns whilst migrants from other regions of the UK and immigrants from the New Commonwealth moved in. Since the 1970s though, growth has been fastest in Buckinghamshire, Hampshire and Oxfordshire, with people here prepared to commute long distances. 36

London has experienced **counter-urbanisation**, as people moved to rural areas where houses were cheaper and the environment more attractive. High levels of car ownership and fast electric railways encouraged people to live further from their work. Motorways like the M4 attracted new industries close to motorway junctions. New jobs created outside London also contributed to counter-urbanisation.

London is still an attractive place to live for many people. The bright lights and opportunities still draw in many young, single people, so that in some parts more than 50 per cent of the households only contain one adult living alone (see Figure 6.10). This is the main reason why London still has a housing shortage, even though its population is decreasing.

During the 1980s and 1990s, some poorer areas of London have become very fashionable addresses. This process is called **gentrification** (see Figure 6.12). In parts of Spitalfields, for example, rich people have chosen to turn old houses into luxury homes, so that they can live near to work and entertainment, reducing the time and cost of commuting.

Figure 6.12 Gentrification in progress in Spitalfields

Causes and effects of migration: making the UK my home

After the 1939–45 war, many industries in the West Midlands urban areas were doing well. In fact, they just could not find enough workers. This was particularly a problem if the jobs were dirty or involved unpleasant hours such as night shifts. Local people did not want these jobs. Some businesses would have closed down if they had not been able to persuade more people to work for them.

At this time, many people in the Commonwealth were looking for a better life for their families. They were attracted by the idea of working for a while in another country such as the UK. They would live cheaply and send home the rest of their earnings. Britain was a good place because they had British passports and some areas, such as the West Midlands, needed them.

HELPING EACH OTHER

If you were planning to work abroad for a while, where would you choose? If you knew that people from your family, or your home area had found work in a certain town, you would probably join them. They would share your religion, speak the same language, understand you and look after you. In this way, different towns in the West Midlands attracted different immigrant communities. By working long hours, they could earn more money here than they had earned in their home country. The original intention was to return home after a while and live in relative luxury.

In the 1960s, the British Government passed laws to limit the number of immigrants. In 1961, there had been five times as many people arriving as ten years earlier. By now though, many of the men had decided to make their homes here. Before new laws in 1968 made it more difficult, or impossible, many wives with their children came to Britain to join their husbands.

The communities are now here to stay. Children born in 1968 and brought up in the West Midlands might now be married, and have their own children too. Many have bought their own homes, and started businesses, such as running shops. All want a good education for their children – another reason for staying in the West Midlands. Now 6.3 per cent of people in the West Midlands region are in families where the parents were born in the countries known as the New Commonwealth and Pakistan.

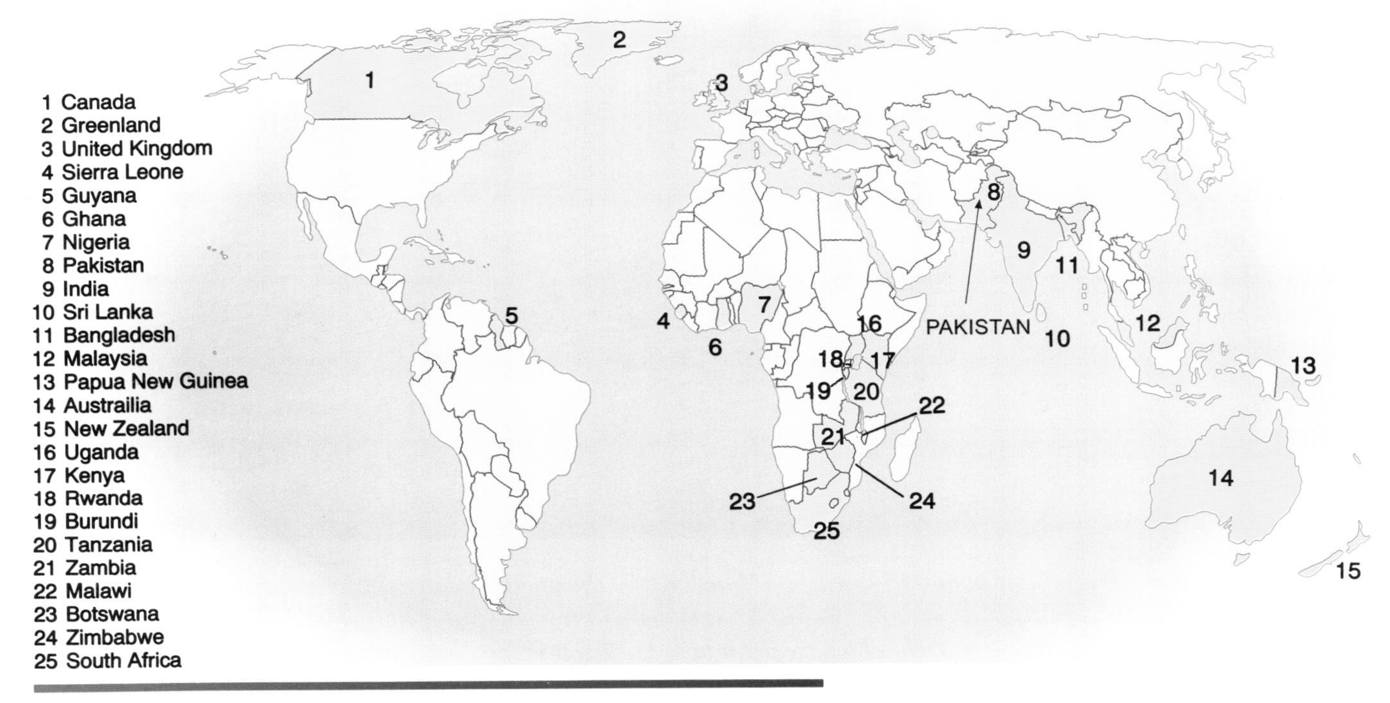

Figure 6.13 The countries of the New Commonwealth and Pakistan

Some communities have integrated with the new arrivals more than others. Some immigrant communities have adapted their traditional way of life, whilst keeping their sense of identity. Many, however, say they have experienced prejudice, being treated differently to the white population. It is often harder for someone from an immigrant background to find a job than a white person with the same qualifications. In some communities, there is tension between white and black youths, more so than between adults, and at times the tension leads to violence.

Figure 6.14 Lye mosque

A WEST MIDLANDS COMMUNITY

Lye is a town which has a Pakistani community. It is in the West Midlands conurbation, 15 km west of Birmingham. Men came here in 1953 from two farming areas near Rawalpindi where it had been hard to make a living. When the Mangla Dam was built to store water for irrigating land south of Rawalpindi some people had to move because it flooded their fields. They had been encouraged to come to Lye by the owner of a local factory which galvanised metal but they were paid lower wages than other workers. They earned about £2 a week, a third of the average wage. Much of this money was sent back to Pakistan to help their families.

Most men did not bring their wives and children to Lye until 1967 or 1968. By 1991, there were 218 Pakistani families in Lye, in a well-established community of 1128 people.

1. List reasons why young men came to the West Midlands from Commonwealth countries in the 1950s and 1960s. At the end of each reason, write either:
   - PUSH if the reason is due to something bad about the country the migrant left, or
   - PULL if it is due to an attraction of the West Midlands.
2. Use an atlas and Figure 6.13 to name three Commonwealth countries from which migrants came to the UK.
3. Draw two columns or use two pages. To the left, list your reasons why communities should mix. To the right, list why they should keep themselves separate.

Figure 6.15 Lye High Street

'We speak Punjabi at home. We are Sunni Muslims, so the meat we have is Halal meat. It has been ritually killed. Through the month of Ramadan, we fast from sunrise to sunset, as our holy book, the Qur'an tells us. The mosque used to be a Christian church which closed down. For us, it is a social centre as well as a place of worship.'

CARING AND SHARING

Figure 6.16 Housing in Lye

Most Pakistani families in Lye own their homes. Twenty-five per cent live in council houses. It is a close community, without social class barriers. There is a strong sense of caring for each other but not much mixing with other local people. Most of the men were farmers before leaving Pakistan and had few industrial skills when they first came to Lye. The manual work they first did has declined because local industry has modernised or closed. Unemployment amongst older men is high. About a third of young and middle aged men run their own businesses, e.g. shops, restaurants. Some are well-qualified professionals, e.g. doctors, accountants.

	0–15	16–retirement	Pensioners
White	1899 (17%)	6847 (63%)	2230 (20%)
Pakistani	557 (49%)	525 (47%)	46 (4%)
All Lye	2495 (20%)	7431 (61%)	2281 (19%)

Figure 6.17 Lye's population in 1991

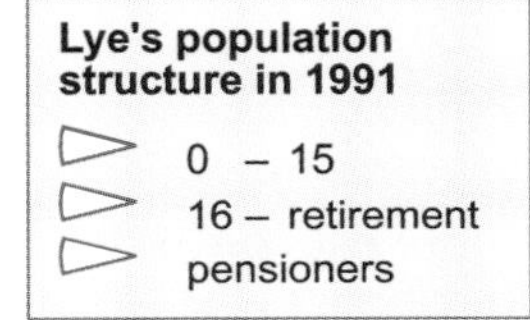

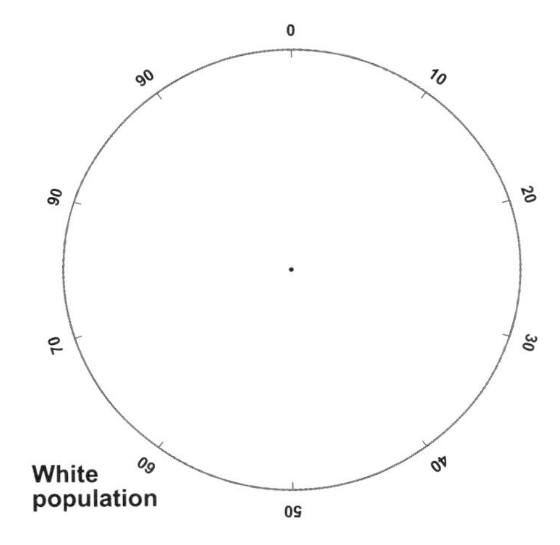

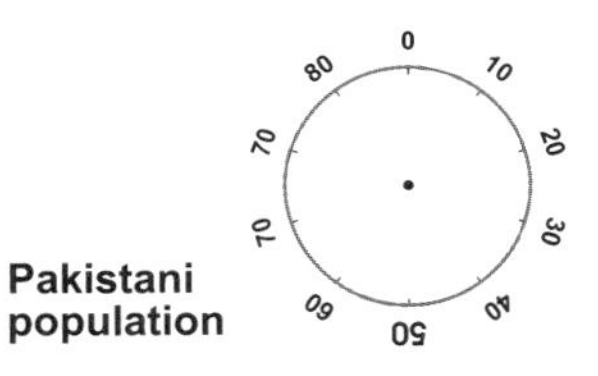

Figure 6.18 Age structure of Lye's white and Pakistani population

Having English and Pakistani roots can provide children with the best of both worlds. Family values are important and children are expected to obey their parents. Girls are often encouraged to marry a relative, usually a cousin. If they are happy with this, parents help to arrange it. Few of the older people, especially the women, can read and write, but many of the children learn Urdu, the written language of Pakistan, at the mosque after school, so that they can read the Qur'an. Most children go to college when they leave school. With a good education, they enjoy a higher standard of living than their parents and are more confident. Over 50 per cent of the families now have 'second generation' children – their parents were born and brought up in Lye. Some older people are unhappy about how some now behave. They think they are not true to the teachings of Islam. Should these second generation children adapt their way of life?

	Pakistanis %	All Lye %
Unemployed (males)	35	16
Owner occupied households	65	56
Single person households	6	26
More than one person per room	49	4
Households without a car	43	40
No central heating	49	33

Figure 6.19 A comparison of indicators for Pakistanis in Lye, and the total Lye population (1991 Census).

4 a What is the average size of a Pakistani family in Lye?
b How does that compare with your family?

5 a Look at Figure 6.17. It shows the number of people in Lye in three age groups. Trace Figure 6.18. The pie charts are drawn so that their size is proportional to the populations. Divide the pie charts to show the two age structures. Use three colours, one for each age group. Add a key.
b What does this show about the proportions in each age group?

6 Look at Figures 6.17 and 6.19.
a What evidence is there that the Pakistani community has many young families?
b How does the Pakistani community compare with the average for Lye in the other figures?

Settlement, location and change: a case study of North East England

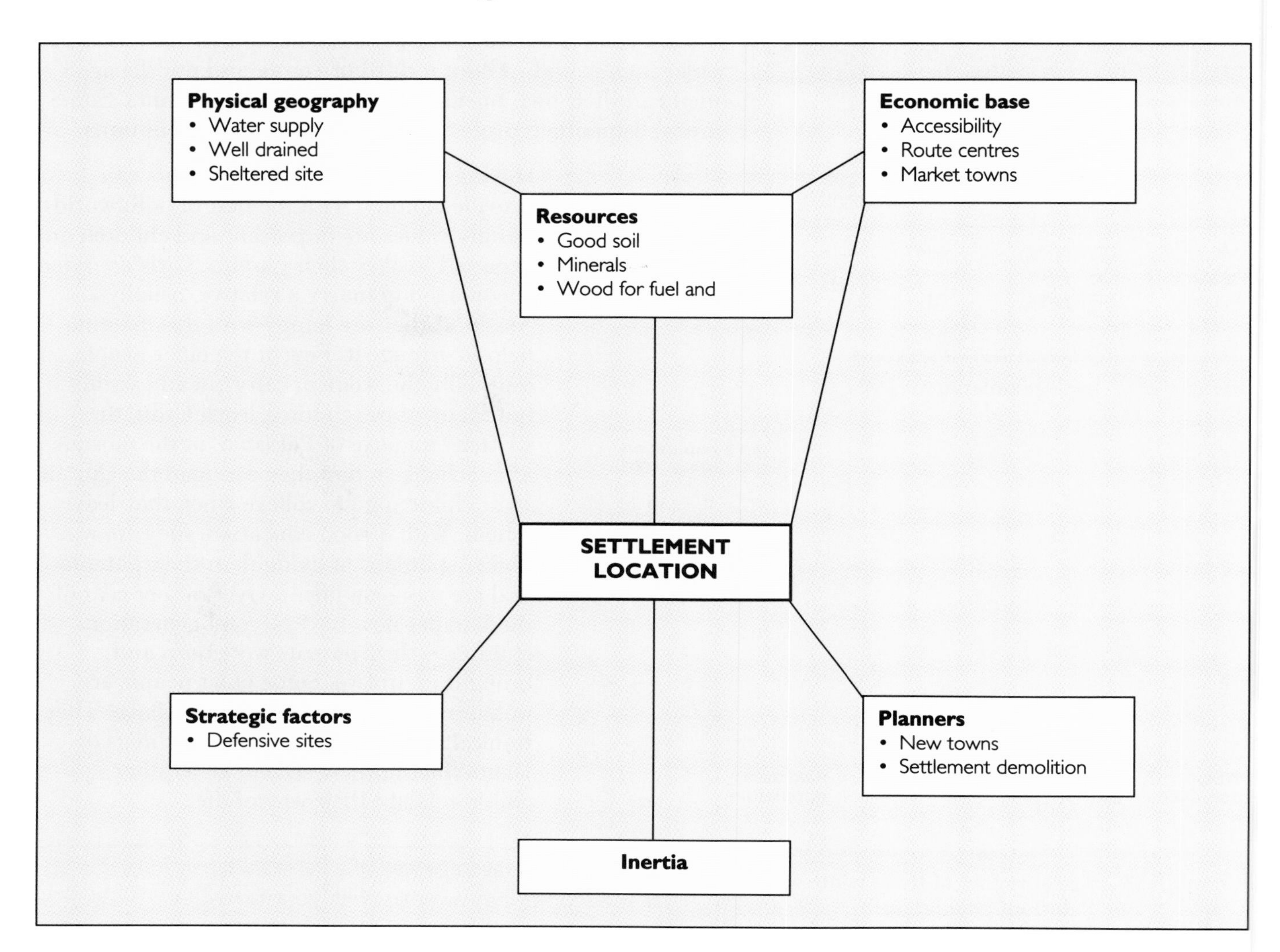

Figure 7.1 Influences on settlement location

Figure 7.1 summarises some of the main influences on settlement location. The most important of these is **inertia** – this is when a settlement continues to grow long after the original reasons for its being there have gone. In the UK many settlements began in locations where there was a river or spring. Because water is now so easily pumped to even quite remote places, this is of course no longer a consideration – and yet the towns and villages remain.

Figure 7.2 summarises the history of settlement change in County Durham over the past few hundred years.

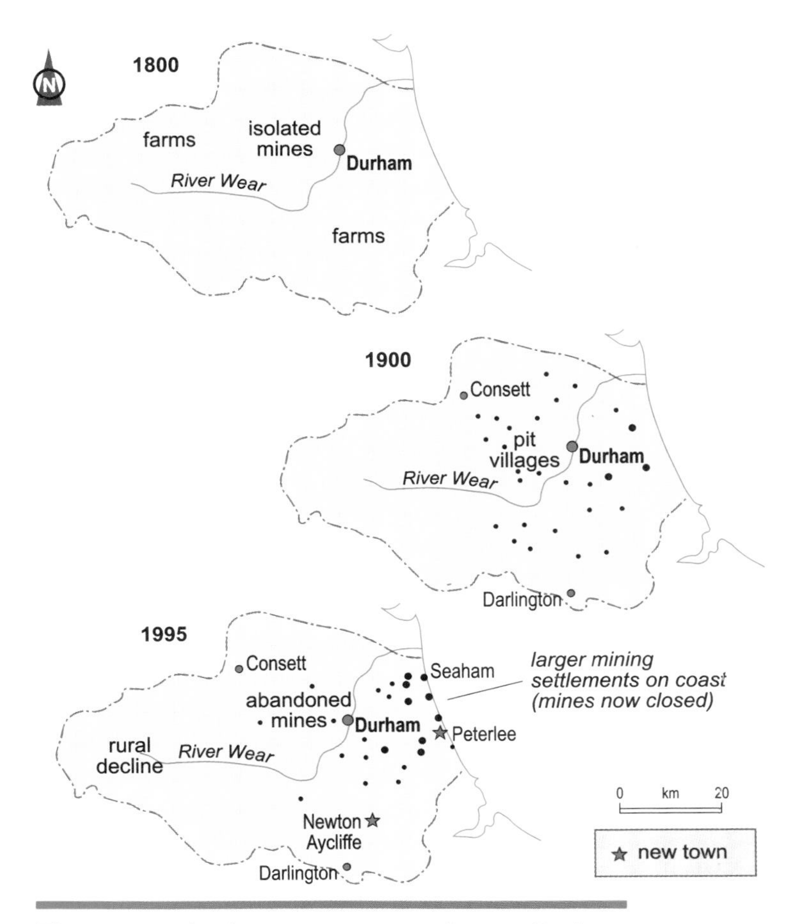

Figure 7.2 Settlement patterns in County Durham

1. Write down a list of all the factors which might have influenced the location of the settlement where you live. Use Figure 7.1 to help you.
2. Why were villages built in west Durham in the nineteenth century?
3. Why did some of the west Durham villages eventually have to be demolished?

BEFORE 1800

Main activity: FARMING

Small villages and farmsteads, the only exception being Durham City which had three roles:

- *Religious.* The body of St Cuthbert was buried here in 995 AD and a cathedral was established in 1093.
- *Military.* The Normans, who invaded Britain in 1066, built a castle in the meander bend of the River Wear to defend England against the Scots.
- *Educational.* The cathedral established a monastery. The monks studied and taught others.

1800–1900

Main activity: COAL MINING

- Coal mines were sunk in the west, where the coal was close to the surface. Around each mine a pit village was built. Iron ore was dug out in some parts, and iron works were built near the mines so the coal could be used for smelting.
- The Industrial Revolution created some new, large towns – Darlington as a railway centre, and Consett for the manufacture of iron.
- The increased efficiency of farming due to the Agricultural Revolution reduced the need for farm workers, and so the rural population fell.
- Durham City established a university in 1832.

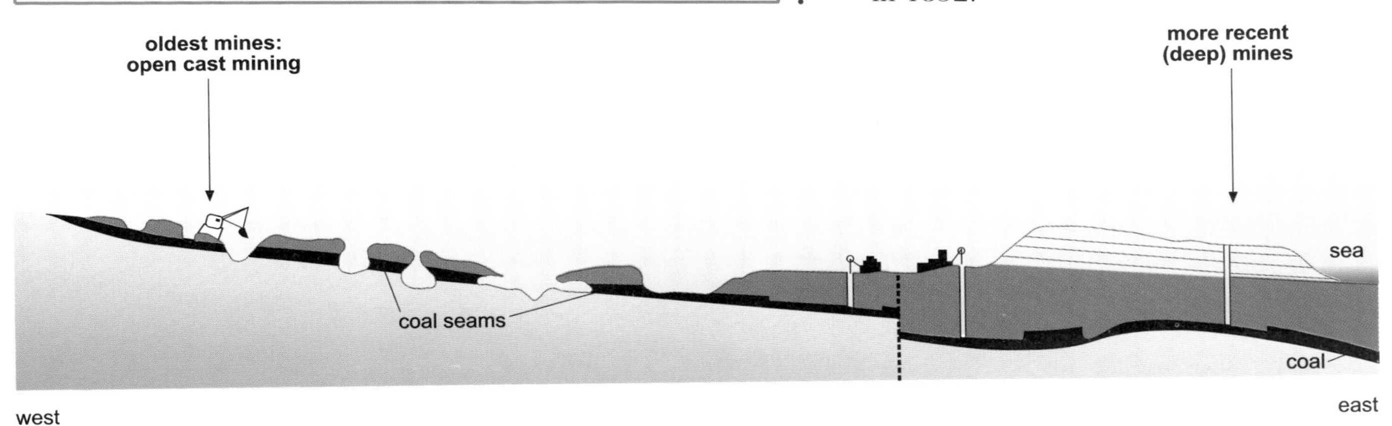

Figure 7.3 Cross-section from west to east across the rocks of County Durham. The coal seams dip towards the sea and are therefore near the surface in the west but deep below the ground in the east

1900–2000

Main activities: DECLINING MINING and MANUFACTURING, GROWING SERVICES

There have been five main changes in the present century.

- The coal in the west of the area began to run out and so new mines were sunk further east. These too had pit villages built around them, some on the coast, e.g. Seaham.
- Where pits closed in the west of the region, most of the settlements lost population and some were actually demolished by Durham County Council under its 1951 Development Plan because they were too expensive to maintain and did not provide any jobs.
- In the far west the farms in the cold, bleak foothills of the Pennines have continued to decline. However, former farming villages within a 30 minute drive of Durham and Newcastle have successfully turned into **dormitory settlements** – lived in by commuters who work in the larger towns.
- Two new towns were built in the county. Newton Aycliffe was developed in 1947 to act as a magnet to attract firms from other parts of England into the area. Peterlee, in 1948, was designed to provide homes and jobs for miners from the closing pit villages in the west.
- Some of the larger towns have declined due to the collapse of industries on which they depended. The steelworks at Consett employed over a third of the men in the town when it closed in 1980, so of course there was a loss of population as people moved to find work elsewhere.

Settlement location: a case study of London

WHY WAS LONDON BUILT WHERE IT WAS?

England was invaded by the Romans in 43 AD and Londinium built as a base from which they could control the South East of England. Figure 7.4 shows why they chose the site. It is remarkable that the centre of the Roman town is still the centre of modern London: the Forum or market place is close to the site of the present Bank of England.

Between 190 and 220 AD a wall was built around the town and parts of this can still be seen today. Gates were built where the wall was crossed by Roman roads, and the names of these gates are still found in modern street names: Newgate, Aldgate, Ludgate, and others.

Many of the main roads in London still follow the line of the original Roman roads. Even the Great Fire of London in 1666, which destroyed much of the town, did little to alter the pattern: people simply rebuilt along the old streets.

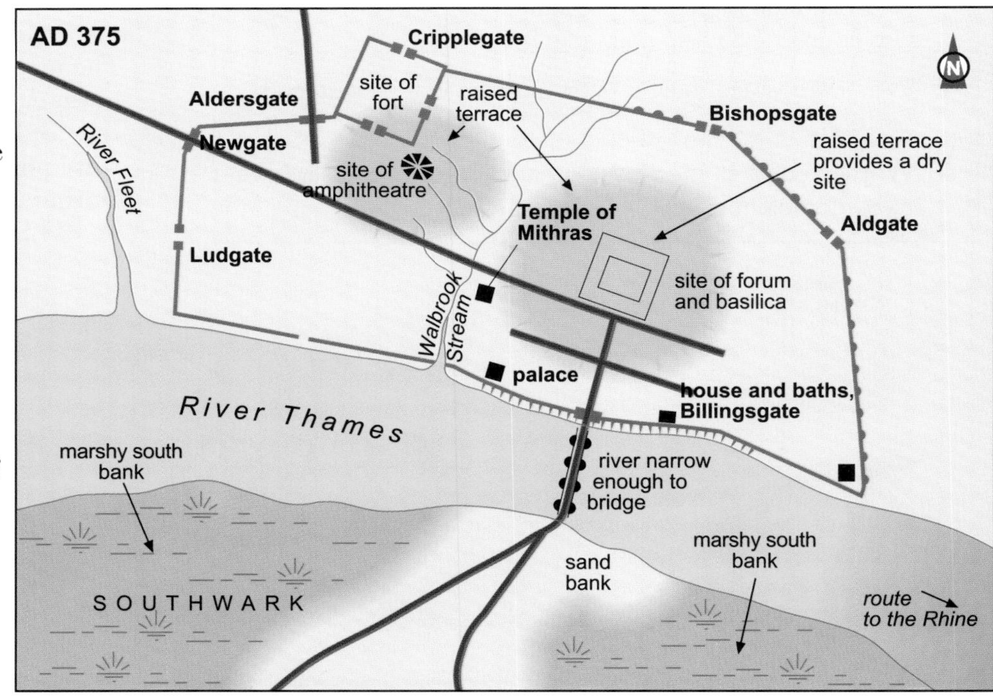

Figure 7.4 Location of Roman London

WHY DID LONDON BECOME A HUGE CITY?

Before 1500 London was little more than a large town (see Figure 7.5). At the time of the Norman Conquest in 1066 the population was only 16 000. With little in the way of sewers or medicine, diseases were a serious problem: the Black Death of 1348–9 killed a third of Londoners.

Growth, based on trade, became faster after 1500, and by 1700 London contained 10 per cent of England's inhabitants – the biggest city in western Europe.

Figure 7.5 shows the fast growth between 1850 and 1900. This happened for three reasons.

- The modernisation of farming (the Agricultural Revolution) meant that fewer farm workers were needed: many came to London to find work.
- Immigrants came from abroad, e.g. the Irish after a severe famine in the 1840s, and Jewish people escaping from eastern Europe in the late nineteenth century.
- Proper sewers were built and clean water was piped to people's houses, so fewer died of disease.

LONDON SINCE 1940

From 1940 to 1980 the population of London fell, especially in the inner city. Many people and firms chose to leave the city for outside areas. This process is known as **counter-urbanisation** and can be divided into two groups.

Positive forces attracted people to places outside London

- Cheaper housing;
- a pleasant environment;
- improved transport enabled people to live outside London but still commute into the city to work;
- new towns built around London after 1946 were designed to draw people away from the capital;
- jobs, since many firms were moving out of London too.

Negative forces pushed people out of London

- High house prices;
- traffic congestion;
- rising crime levels
- a poor environment;
- unemployment;
- demolition of older houses by local authorities.

Since 1980 the higher birth rate in London has caused the population to rise again slightly. Today, with a population of 6.7 million, London is the tenth largest city in the world.

1. Using Figure 7.4 write down five reasons why the Romans chose the site of Londinium.
2. Draw two graphs using the data given in figure 7.5, one showing population growth from 60–1500 AD and the other showing population change between 1600–2000 AD. Mark the following on your graph: Norman invasion of Britain; Black Death; Great Fire of London; Agricultural Revolution; Irish Famine; and the Second World War (1939–45).

Year	Population
AD 60	30 000
300	50 000
1066	16 000
1200	25 000
1350	50 000
1500	100 000
1600	200 000
1700	600 000
1800	1 000 000
1850	2 600 000
1900	6 500 000
1940	8 600 000
1970	7 400 000
1990	6 700 000
2000 (estimate)	6 700 000

Figure 7.5 Population of London

Settlement location and layout: a case study of Milton Keynes New Town

WHY WAS MILTON KEYNES BUILT?

Milton Keynes is the largest of the new towns which have been built since 1946 in southern England (see Figure 7.6). The aim of most of the new towns was to stop larger cities from growing any more: they were **overspill towns** to accommodate people and firms moving out of expanding cities. Most of the firms and people in Milton Keynes have come from London and some other overcrowded parts of the South East.

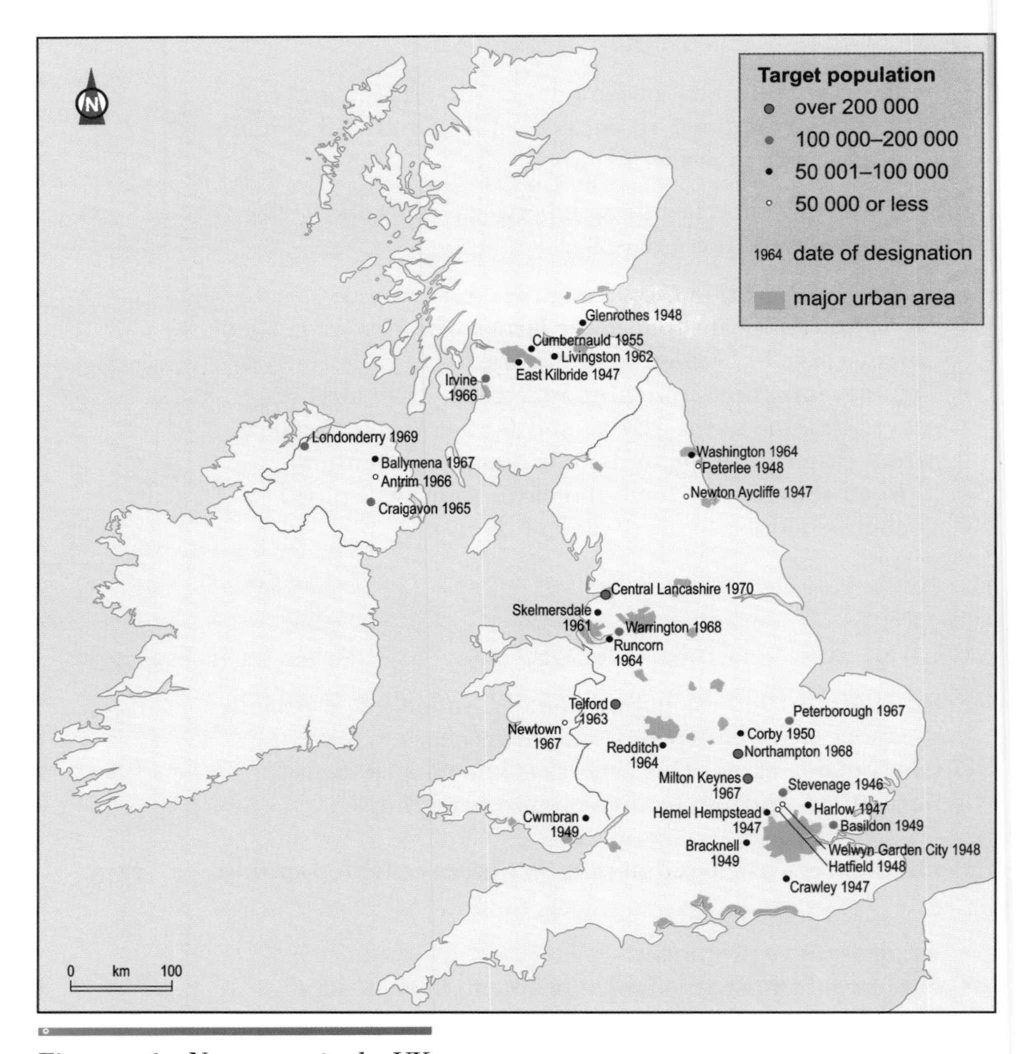

Figure 7.6 New towns in the UK

HOW WAS THE SITE CHOSEN?

The site of Milton Keynes was chosen in 1967. It had a number of advantages.

- A large flat area of farmland;
- close to the M1, Britain's main north–south motorway, and the London to Scotland railway line;
- halfway between London and Birmingham, the two biggest cities in the UK.

Forty thousand people already lived in the area before the town was built. Some lived in the town of Bletchley, but others were in small villages, all of which were to become small parts of the huge new town.

HOW HAS THE TOWN GROWN?

Originally the planners expected the town to grow to a population of 250 000 – this is called the **target population**. Because the birth rate has fallen and planners want to prevent more firms leaving the big cities the population will probably not go above 200 000. Today the population is 150 000 and the town is still growing.

The main way in which Milton Keynes has grown is by the migration of firms from the London area into the town. These firms bring many of their workers with them, most of whom are under the age of 40 and have young families.

Figure 7.7 Milton Keynes

WHY IS THE TOWN LAYOUT AS IT IS?

Figure 7.7 shows the layout of the town. The key idea behind the plan was that in the future most people would own cars. To make sure there was no traffic congestion the following was done.

- The whole town is organised around a grid of main roads, forming squares about 1 km across;
- offices and factories are not concentrated in one area (which might cause congestion) but scattered in many different parts of the city – these are the purple areas in Figure 7.7;
- there is a huge amount of parking space provided.

The following measures were implemented to protect people from the impact of cars.

- All housing was built well away from the roads, shielded by banks and trees – 15 million trees and shrubs have been planted;
- a system of paths called *redways* were laid out for cyclists and pedestrians away from the roads – where they cross a main road they do so by an underpass or bridge;
- the main shopping centre is fully pedestrianised.

Within each grid square is a housing estate. Each estate has its own style of architecture and its own name. Each has a primary school and a few shops. Within each estate the houses are both big and small, for sale and for rent: this ensures that each estate has a variety of types of people.

Figure 7.8 The redways allow people to walk around the town while avoiding roads

1. Why was Milton Keynes built?
2. Why has the target population been reduced?
3. Why was the site of the new town chosen?
4. Describe and explain the road system in the town.
5. What is the redways system?
6. Why are jobs scattered about the town as they are?
7. Why are there fewer old people in Milton Keynes compared to towns in the rest of the UK?
8. What do you think are the disadvantages of living in a new town like Milton Keynes?

Settlement growth: a case study of the London suburbs

Of a current London population of 6.7 million, 4.2 million live in outer London – the suburbs. These suburbs grew with great speed between 1850–1935, especially in the ten year period after 1925. This explosion happened for a number of reasons.

Figure 7.9 A 1930s advertisement for private houses being built along new railway lines on the edge of London

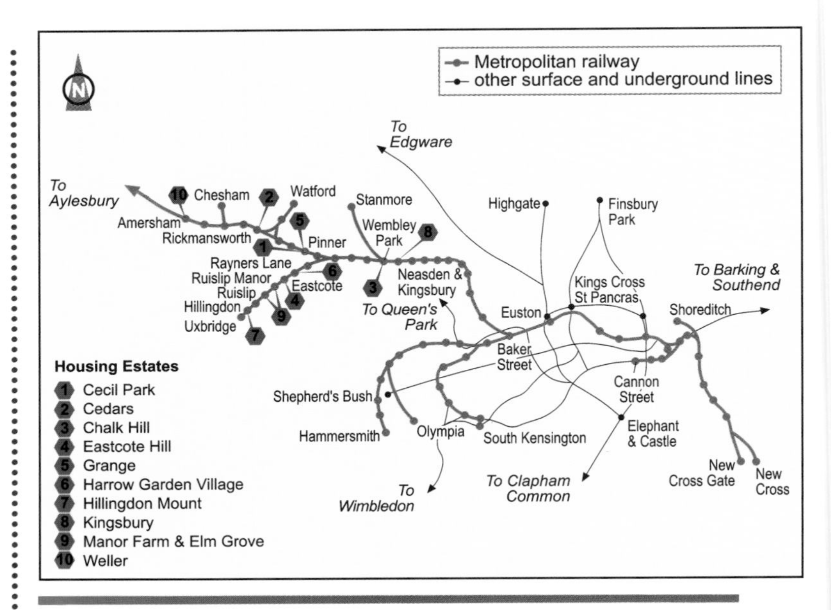

Figure 7.10 The Metropolitan Railway Company's lines and housing estates in 1932

- The development of new forms of transport enabled people to live in the suburbs and yet work in the centre of London. The horse-drawn omnibus was the first development, but the railways were much more important – both above and below ground. Much of north west London, for example, was built because the Metropolitan Railway Company developed lines to Swiss Cottage (1868), Harrow (1880) and Aylesbury (1892). In order to make money the Metropolitan Railway Company decided to build, not only the railway lines, but also estates of houses around the stations. The area became known as *Metroland*. The new railway lines encouraged people to come and buy these houses, and people living on the estates used the railway to get to work.
- People wanted to buy houses. Before 1920 most people did not own their houses: they rented from a landlord. During the period from 1920–39 there was a rapid increase in the number of middle-income people who were able to buy a house. They were helped by the development of building societies who lent money: a loan to buy a house is called a *mortgage*. Many of the new suburban houses were built for people who wished to buy a house rather than rent one.
- The environment of the suburbs was much nicer than that of the inner city. Some of the new estates were called garden suburbs because they had large gardens and plenty of trees.

- Council estates were also built in the suburbs during the period 1920–38. These were built to provide homes for poorer people to rent. They were needed because so many families were either homeless or lived in slums in inner London. At Becontree in north east London, for example, an estate was built with a population of 120 000 – the largest development of this kind in the world.

The sudden explosive growth of the suburbs produced a city which was vastly bigger in size, as Figure 7.11 shows. It was becoming difficult for poorer people who lived near the centre of the city to ever get out to the countryside. Houses and factories were eating up the countryside at a horrifying rate – this sudden spread of buildings was called *sprawl*. After 1940 planners decided to stop London's growth by creating a belt of land around the capital within which building was restricted: this is called the *Green Belt*. 42

1 Look at Figure 7.11. Describe the differences between suburban and inner city areas under the following headings:
  a density of population;
  b age of houses;
  c design of houses;
  d the sort of people who live there.

2 What were the main reasons for the growth of the London suburbs?

3 Why did the London suburbs eventually stop growing?

Figure 7.11 Contrasting inner city and suburban boroughs

Homes for Londoners: a case study of urban land use

1 Using Figure 7.13 draw a line graph showing the changing pattern of housing tenure for inner London between 1950 and 1990: you will need to draw three lines, one for each of the three types of tenure.

2 Write out the following sentences pairing up those in the top box with those in the bottom box.

A There was a rise in the proportion of local authority houses after 1950 because
B There has been a general decline in the number of private landlords prepared to rent houses because
C We would expect more people to be able to afford to buy their own homes because
D After 1980 there was a fall in the number of council houses because

E in 1980 the government passed a law forcing local authorities to sell council houses to residents who wished to buy them.
F after that date local authorities built many estates.
G people have on average become richer.
H they have been put off renting their houses to other people because laws make it difficult for them to move these tenants out if they want to.

3 Figure 7.12 shows the location of council housing in London. Using the information on Figure 6.11, page 27, explain why such a high proportion of the council housing is in the East End.

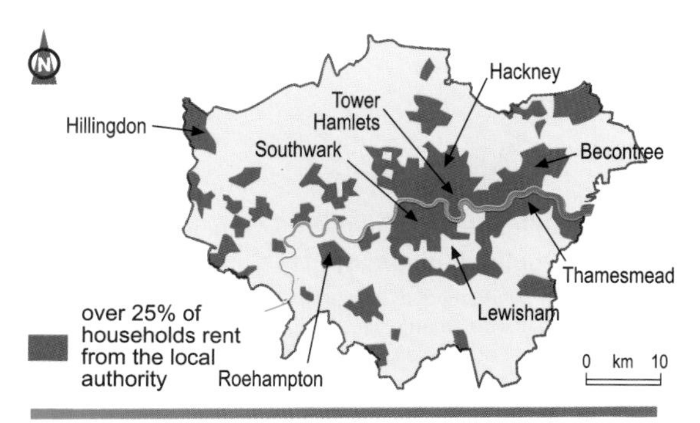

Figure 7.12 Areas in which over 25 per cent of households rent from the local authority

DO LONDONERS OWN THEIR HOMES?

Whether or not people own their home or rent, their occupancy is called **housing tenure**. There are three main types of housing tenure.

- People who own their homes;
- people who rent their homes from the local authority;
- people who rent their homes from a private landlord or housing association. A housing association is a charity which provides housing for people on low incomes.

Figure 7.13 shows the way the balance between the three forms of housing tenure has changed over the past 40 years.

Year	Owner occupiers	Renting from a private landlord or housing association	Renting from a local authority
1950	28	56	16
1960	33	47	20
1970	40	35	25
1980	48	21	31
1990	57	20	23

Figures represent percentage of households in London

Figure 7.13 Housing tenure in London

Figure 7.14 Demolition of a tower block in Hackney

CARDBOARD CITY

A shortage of good housing is one of the most important problems facing many Londoners. Although we often see pictures of people living on the streets (sleeping rough) this is only a small part of the story. In the early 1990s there were over 30 000 families registered as homeless, most living temporarily in bed and breakfast hotels. Many people live in houses which are overcrowded or suffer from problems such as damp. There are a number of reasons for this problem.

- The demand for housing is going up. Despite London's population falling in recent years, the number of households has risen: a household is one or more people who live together in a house or flat. Whereas 50 years ago a typical London household would have been a mother, father and four children, today it would be one or two people living on their own. In inner London, in 1991, 38.1 per cent of households consisted of one person. More households mean more houses are needed.
- Not enough new houses have been built for people on lower incomes to rent or buy.
- Existing houses cost so much that lower paid people cannot afford them.
- Some houses are old and have become run down: 35 per cent of London's houses were built before 1920.
- Many modern flats have been badly built or designed.

WHAT SORT OF HOUSES DO PEOPLE LIKE TO LIVE IN?

In the period between 1955–75, streets of Victorian houses were demolished by local authorities because they were old and lacked modern amenities. They were rebuilt as blocks of flats, which were fashionable at the time. Many of the flats are only four or five stories high with long walkways which enable residents to reach the front doors: **deck-access** flats. Although some of these were better than the previous slums, many were not. They suffer from a number of problems.

- Using space for large areas of grass around the flats meant there were not enough new homes to rehouse all those whose houses had been demolished. Some residents, therefore, were forced to leave the area.
- Communities of friends and relatives were broken up when their homes were demolished.
- The flats had no private gardens and the green areas around them were unsafe for children playing.
- Deck-access flats without secure entrances were especially hard to police: muggings and burglaries became a problem.
- Local councils did not maintain the flats well and they soon became run down. Lifts were often out of order.
- Some flats suffered from damp, or from plagues of insects which bred behind the walls.

Figure 7.15 The Aylesbury estate in south London as it was in 1890 and as it is today. © Crown Copyright

Since 1975 local authorities and housing associations have preferred to build normal two storey houses. Instead of pulling down old houses they modernise them. The government provides money (**grants**) for this work.

Land use and social conflict: a case study of the rural–urban fringe of Hertfordshire

Figure 7.17 shows an area of Hertfordshire just north of London. It is largely countryside, but because it is close to London it has been affected by the city in many ways.

This area is all within the Green Belt. The Green Belt is an area of land around London within which building is restricted. The aim of the Green Belt policy was to stop London growing: planners were worried that the city was becoming too big. It was also hoped that the Green Belt could become an attractive area for Londoners to visit. You can see from Figure 7.17 that there are some large towns in the Green Belt: these existed before the Green Belt policy began in 1938.

LAND USE CONFLICTS

Because the area is close to London it is under all sorts of pressures which are not normally felt in the countryside, and these tend to damage the appearance or quality of the land. Sometimes one land use damages another: this causes land use conflict.

	% of farmers affected
Any trespassers	88
Trespass resulting in damage	78
Rubbish dumping	71
Horseriding	36
Theft of crops/livestock	16
Motorcycling	11

Figure 7.16 Results of a survey into farmers' views of the problem of trespassing on land, south Hertfordshire

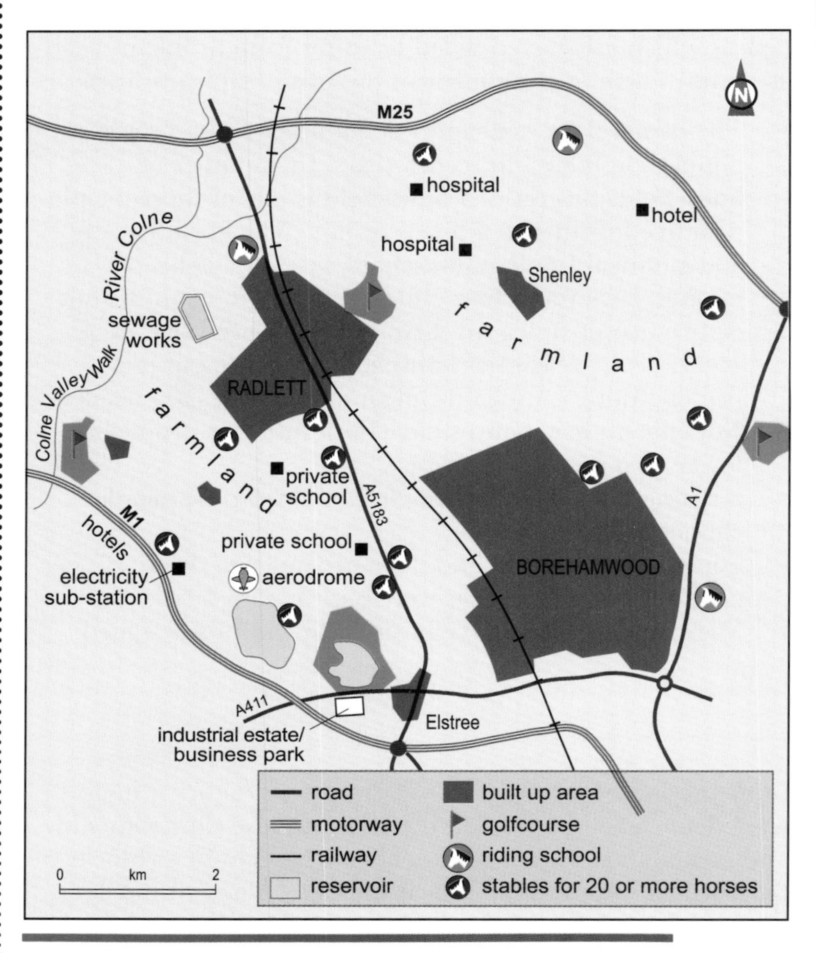

Figure 7.17 Land use in the rural-urban fringe of south Hertfordshire

Farming

The main land use in this part of Hertfordshire is farming, but the farms are very unlike those in remoter parts of the country. Their close proximity to the city means that they suffer from people trespassing on the land (Figure 7.16). Most of the trespassers are young people from housing estates immediately next to the farm, although horseriders are also regarded as a nuisance. The problems created by people leaving gates open and by dogs have persuaded many farmers to change from livestock to arable farming. Farms have been damaged by the building of roads, especially the M25, which in some cases have gone right through the middle of a farm. Farmers are forced to sell their land for this purpose and this is called **compulsory purchase**

Being close to a city is not all bad: there are certain advantages too.

- Fields can be rented to people who live in the city for grazing horses. In fact, this is one of the most common land uses in the area.
- Farm-gate sales: farms on busy roads attract customers to buy produce direct from a farm shop.
- Pick-your-own: fruit growers can attract people from the city to pick their own fruit direct from the field.
- Green Belt farmers can easily pick up temporary workers from the city to work during harvest time.

Figure 7.18 Horses grazing in fields let by farmers near Heathrow

Some farms have been bought by people who work in London but like to live on a farm – partly because the farm is an attractive place to live, partly as an investment, or for prestige. These farms are called *hobby farms* and are often run by farm managers. They tend to specialise in types of produce which do not require much labour, e.g. beef cattle or grain.

Figure 7.19 Reclaimed gravel pit in Grays, Essex

Gravel extraction

Gravel is used for building – it is often mixed to become concrete. It is very profitable and some farmers have sold their land to gravel companies. During the period while the gravel is being scraped out, local people are disturbed by the large lorries which come to take gravel away. When the extraction has finished the land is either flooded and becomes a lake or reservoir, or it is restored. Unfortunately it is never possible to restore land fully: the original trees have gone, and the soil is of a poor quality.

Reservoirs

Reservoirs are needed to supply cities with water. Sometimes they develop out of gravel pits. Often the reservoirs are used for sailing and canoeing, but because roads have to be diverted around them they can increase journey lengths and times for local people.

Land use	% of area 1970	1980	1990
Agriculture	69	66	60
Recreation	5	7	8
Woodland	10	7	5
Built up area	5	6	8
Institutions (hospitals, schools)	4	5	6
Utilities (gas, water, electricity)	1	1	1
Mineral extraction	3	4	4
Other	3	4	8

Figure 7.20 Land use in south Hertfordshire

Sanitary landfill

Figure 7.21 A water storage reservoir

Areas on the edges of cities are often used for dumping rubbish. Pits may be dug and filled with waste. Old gravel pits are often used. At the end of the process soil is put back on top.

Sanitary landfill creates a number of problems – the nuisance of lorries delivering the waste, the litter and smell which the dump produces, and the poor quality of land which is left at the end. Sometimes the rotting waste produces pockets of methane gas under the ground, which can explode.

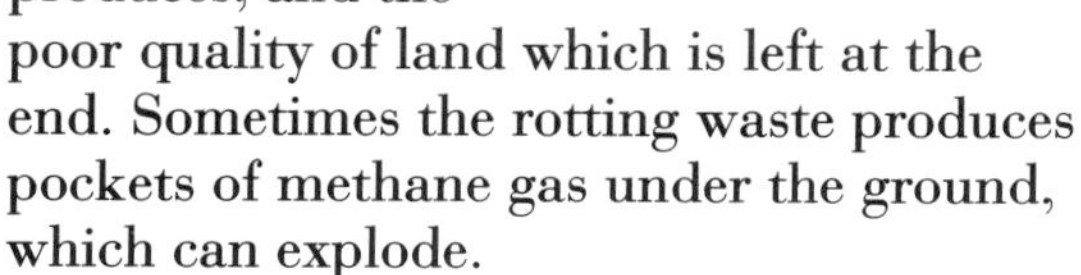

Fly-tipping

Illegal dumping of household waste and garden rubbish, and occasionally of builders' rubble, is common in the urban fringe.

Speculative holding of land

Quite large pieces of land look very run down. One reason for this is that property companies buy up fields hoping that in future years they will either sell at a profit, or that they will obtain permission to develop the land. This is called *speculative holding*.

1. Name three types of recreational activity shown in Figure 7.17.
2. What land use conflicts might exist between those who wish to develop the Green Belt for recreational use and the other land uses described in this section?
3. Which of the land uses described in this section actually help those wishing to develop recreational facilities in the area?

Institutions and utilities

The urban fringe is sometimes regarded by central and local government as a place to put the services for the city which cannot be easily contained in the city itself, e.g. sewage works, electricity sub-stations, prisons, and psychiatric hospitals.

Road building

Completed in 1986, the M25 was built right through the middle of the Green Belt. It was designed to relieve congestion in London by allowing traffic to by-pass the capital city. Because it is impossible to cross the motorway except where the few bridges or tunnels have been built, the motorway acts as a barrier to movement within the area.

Building development

Despite the fact that building is supposed to be restricted in the Green Belt, new building has been permitted adjacent to existing settlements. Since 1980 the largest number of new buildings have been offices, hotels, and retail warehouses (large stores selling DIY goods, carpets and furniture).

Recreation

Because it is close to the city, areas like south Hertfordshire have been developed to provide recreational opportunities for people from the city.

Figure 7.22 The village of Shenley which has undergone social change since 1960

SOCIAL CONFLICT

Although there are some big towns in south Hertfordshire, most people live in villages. Originally these were farming villages, but since 1960 many people who work in London have moved in. This was made possible by the increased ownership of cars: commuters could easily drive to work or to the nearest railway station.

Conflicts of interest arose between local people and the newcomers. The original inhabitants envied the high incomes and lifestyle of the new arrivals. They came to resent the fact that the price of houses was pushed up so that young local people could no longer afford to buy homes there.

	1960	1970	1980	1990
Total population ('000s)	800	900	950	900
% of population – unskilled manual workers	35	30	20	12
– professional/managerial	5	7	9	24
% of workforce employed locally	58	45	30	12
% of households owning a car	27	52	79	88
Number of shops	12	8	7	4

Figure 7.23 Data about the population of Shenley, south Hertfordshire

	Original inhabitants	Newcomers
Income	Low	High
Level of car ownership		
How many local friends?		
How many local relatives?		Few
Distance of travel to work		Long way

Figure 7.24 Table of characteristics of the original residents and newcomers living in Shenley

4 Look at Figure 7.23. Describe how the village changed between 1960 and 1990.

5 Make a copy of Figure 7.24 and fill in the blanks; some of the answers have already been done for you.

6 Why do you think the original inhabitants resented the arrival of the newcomers?

THE DIFFERENCES BETWEEN PRIMARY, SECONDARY AND TERTIARY INDUSTRIES

Different types of industries

People work in many different types of industries, and these can usually be divided into three groups. People's jobs are described as being in a **primary industry** if they are involved in getting a **resource** from the natural environment, e.g. farmers, miners or fisherman; in **secondary industries** if they make or manufacture goods, e.g. factory workers or builders; and in **tertiary** (or **service**) **industries** if they provide a service for other people or companies, e.g. teachers, shopkeepers, bus drivers or policemen. Another way of dividing up the types of jobs which people do is shown in Figure 8.1. The different number of people in each type of job is called the **employment structure**.

The types of jobs which people do in the UK are changing all the time. This chapter investigates some of the changes in employment structure by looking at some examples of different types of industries from around the UK.

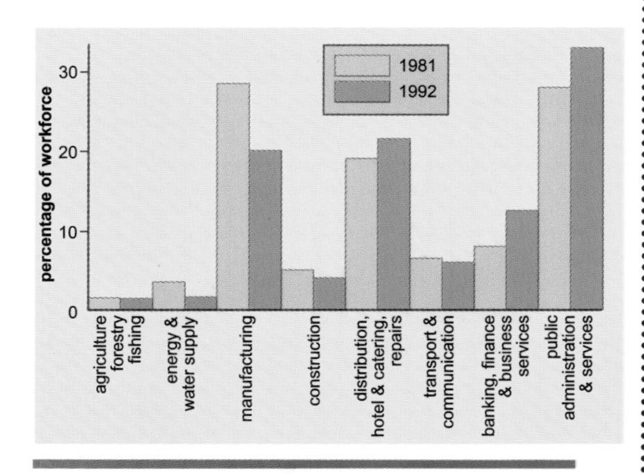

Figure 8.1 Employment change in the UK 1981–1992

1. In your own words, explain what is meant by a primary, a secondary and a tertiary worker, giving three examples of each, other than those listed.
2. Study Figure 8.1.
   - **a** Which type of jobs was most important in 1981 and in 1992?
   - **b** Which type of industry employed the fewest people in both 1981 and 1992?
   - **c** Which five types of industry have had a reduction in their share of the total workforce between 1981 and 1992?
   - **d** Which types of industry have had an increasing share of the total workforce between 1981 and 1992?
3. In Figure 8.1 there are eight different categories of jobs, e.g. agriculture, forestry and fishing; manufacturing, etc. Make a table to show whether each of the eight categories is Primary, Secondary or Tertiary.
4. **a** Carry out a survey of all the jobs that the adults living in the homes of your classmates do.
   - **b** Draw a graph of your results, similar to Figure 8.1.
   - **c** Describe the differences between your class results and Figure 8.1.
   - **d** What does this tell you about the jobs type in the area around your school?

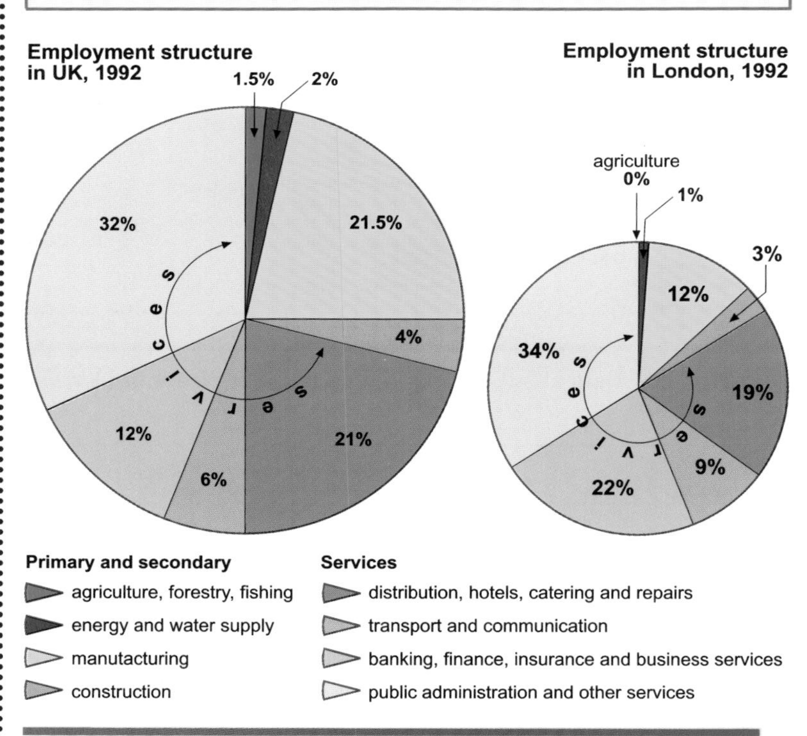

Figure 8.2 Employment structure in London and the UK 1992

The changing location of tertiary industries: a case study of London

Service industries are now the most important type of industry in the UK and London is the most important centre of this industry in the country. 3.5 million people work in London, most of them in the service industries (see Figure 8.2). The largest employers are the borough councils (who run local services such as education, housing and roads), the National Health Service, and the Civil Service and these come under the heading of Public Administration in Figure 8.2.

RECORD LONDON JOBS EXODUS

London is suffering as it loses jobs at an accelerating rate. The number of people whose jobs are being moved away from the capital is over 1000 each month.

Government departments which have left London include the DSS which has moved to Leeds, the Inland Revenue, which has moved a large part of its operation to Nottingham, and the Patent and the Central Statistical Offices, which have moved to Newport, Gwent. The Post Office, British Telecom, Pearl Assurance and the Bank of England have also moved out of London in search of cheaper office space and lower wage costs.

Some offices have moved long distances, for example, the entire head office of Shell Chemicals UK has moved from London to Chester, and Barclays Bank has moved 1000 jobs to Coventry. Many have only moved into the suburbs, such as Ealing, Hammersmith and especially Croydon, where offices are cheaper and employees can get to work more easily.

Figure 8.4 Office decentralisation from London

THE CLUSTERING OF OFFICES

Many of the office jobs in London are found in just two small areas: the City and Westminster. The City is dominated by offices and is the financial heart of the capital. In 1991, only 4000 people lived there. The area is surrounded by mainline railway stations, so people can get to work easily. Some offices locate here because they need to be near particular buildings: insurance brokers are based in and near Lloyd's, and the headquarters of main banks like to be near the Bank of England.

The banking, trading and insurance industries began in the City because London was an important port. London has grown to be the most important centre for banking in the world. The City area has many high-tech communication links with other important world cities and has attracted financial companies from many countries.

The Houses of Parliament and Downing Street are in Westminster with many government offices and Departments close by.

The West End is the entertainment centre of London and contains most of the theatres, department stores, exclusive shops, hotels and restaurants.

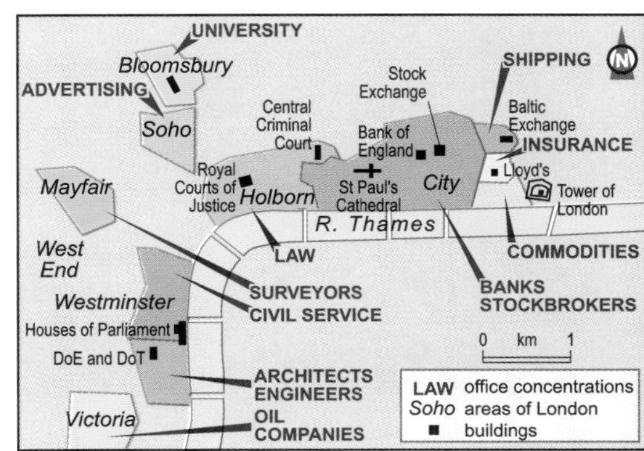

Figure 8.3 Office concentrations in central London

1. Study Figure 8.2. **a** What percentage of all the UK's employees work in the service industries? **b** What percentage of London's employees work in services?
2. Why does London have a higher percentage of jobs in public administration and other services than the rest of the UK?
3. Study Figure 8.3.
   - **a** Why do you think the main solicitors and legal company offices are in the Holborn area?
   - **b** Why do you think companies choose to be in the same part of the City as others which do the same type of work?
4. Read Figure 8.4.
   - **a** *'London is suffering'*. What do you think is meant by this?
   - **b** Why is the number of office jobs in the city decreasing?
   - **c** Give two reasons why companies are leaving London.
   - **d** Why do you think some companies choose to move long distances to their new offices and others only a short distance to the suburbs?
5. Computers and modern communications mean that more people can work from home. How might this affect location and number of offices in the next few years?

Agriculture, a primary economic activity: case study 1: Willow Tree Farm, a large arable farm

BRIEF RECENT HISTORY

This very large farm consists of three types of land tenure. The Brantons are Lord Carrington's tenants on part of the land; they farm some of it under contract for him, and they own the rest. Originally, the farm was 10 ha in size. Over recent years, this has increased as other farms in the area have been incorporated.

The advantages of having such a large farm unit are that economies of scale can be made. This means that the inputs for the farm can be bought in bulk, saving money and spreading the cost of all the expensive equipment more evenly. Chemical fertilisers, weedkillers, fungicides and aphidicides are used to produce high quality crops and a high yield: about 10 tonnes of wheat per ha (the national average is about 7.5 tonnes per hectare).

The farm receives less than 600 mm of rainfall each year, which is wet enough for cereals, but not for grass so there are no pastoral farms in the area. It is so dry that the potato crop has to be irrigated using a large portable spray over the summer before it is harvested. The soil is light and ideal for growing arable crops efficiently, which can easily be harvested using machines. Harvest Festivals are in October, although harvesting is now done earlier, mostly in August. A rotation system is used (see Figure 8.5) which means that different nutrients in the soil will be used each year and any pest or disease which thrives on a particular crop will have little chance of survival, even if it survives the hard winter frosts.

In the last few years the Brantons have had to cope with a number of changes. Apart from the winters getting much milder, the government now pays farmers not to farm 15 per cent of their land and have stopped them from burning the straw from their fields.

Year 1	wheat
Year 2	potatoes
Year 3	wheat
Year 4	sugar beet
Year 5	wheat
Year 6	peas or linseed
Year 7	wheat

Figure 8.5 Rotation on Willow Tree Farm

FARM FACTFILE

Name:	Willow Tree Farm
Location:	Deeping Fen, 3 km to the south west of Spalding, South Lincolnshire.
Size:	1000 ha.
Owners:	Mr and Mrs W D Branton and Lord Carrington.
Workforce:	7 full-time and part-time labourers during harvest.
Animals:	None.
Crops grown:	Winter wheat; sugar beet; oil seed rape; linseed; peas; potatoes; daffodil bulbs; strawberries; raspberries.
Equipment:	2 combine harvesters; tractors; potato and sugar beet harvesters; refrigerated potato store; other assorted arable equipment.
Type of soil:	80 per cent Grade 2*; 20 per cent Grade 1*. Some soil is light silt and some is the heavy clay remains of peat.
Produce sold:	Wheat; linseed; rape seed; potatoes; dried peas; sugar beet; daffodil bulbs; strawberries and raspberries.

*Grade 1 is the best land for agriculture on a scale of 1–5.

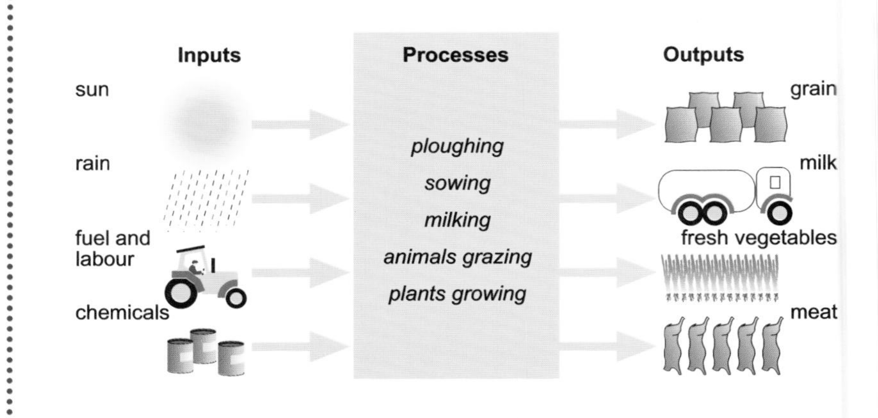

Figure 8.6 The farming system

Figure 8.7 Harvesting wheat on Willow Tree Farm

Figure 8.8 Refrigerated potato store on Willow Tree Farm

1. Using Figure 8.6, draw a systems diagram to show the inputs, processes and outputs of the farm.
2. How will the milder winters affect the farm?
3. Why do you think straw burning is not allowed any more?
4. What is straw used for in other parts of the country?
5. Why do the Brantons get paid not to farm some of their land?
6. They get paid a figure for each hectare which they do not farm. This is worked out using the national average. Do Mr and Mrs Branton gain or lose from this calculation?
7. Why can the crops be harvested earlier now?
8. With the earlier harvest, which people in the area can help?

Case study 2: Aspinall House Farm, a mixed dairy farm

FARM FACTFILE

Name:	Aspinall House Farm.
Location:	Douglas Valley, Dalton (4 km west of Wigan).
Size:	350 ha.
Owners:	The Hodge family.
Workforce:	Five full-time, including one dairyman and two brothers.
Animals:	200 dairy cows; 120 beef cows; 5 bulls.
Crops grown:	Maize; wheat; barley; beans; rape.
Equipment:	Milking parlour; tractors; combine harvester; assorted arable equipment.
Type of soil:	22 ha of Grade 1. The rest Grade 2 or 3. Wetter soils in the field near the river. Drier soils on Ashurst Ridge.
Produce sold:	Milk; some crops.

BRIEF RECENT HISTORY

This family-owned farm has seen many changes recently. In 1980, it was 100 ha in size and there was a dairy herd of 70 cows. 50 ha of **cereal crops** (wheat and barley) were grown to feed to the animals and about 6 ha were used to grow **cash crops** (carrots, swedes and potatoes) to sell. By 1983, oil seed rape and beans to feed the cattle were being grown instead of some of the other cereals because the EU paid more money for these crops.

Over the next few years, the prices which the EU paid for produce came down and farmers in the area found it difficult to make money; many left farming.

The Hodge family has now taken over some of these other farms and so has increased the size of its farm. By 1987, they had two dairy herds and 350 ha, 175 ha of grass and 175 ha of crops, altogether.

The eldest son, James, has now taken over the running of the farm from his father. James has made some more changes because the factors affecting farming have changed again.

Figure 8.9 Cattle shed and slurry tank

Figure 8.10 Milk being collected

- James prefers keeping animals to growing crops.
- Each dairy herd needs a dairyperson to look after it.
- Wages is one of the largest bills to be paid.
- There are two sets of expensive farm buildings which are for keeping cows.
- Fresh milk is always needed in the large towns.
- A new way of feeding maize to cows has been developed.
- Cows eat wheat and barley grown on the farm.
- Cows eat bought proteins, e.g. soya beans, fish meal.
- Grass is used to graze cows on and to cut and make into silage which provides a winter feed for cows.
- Nobody in the family has ever kept sheep or any other animals, apart from cattle.

Figure 8.11 Keeping animals on Aspinall House Farm

- Vegetables require a lot of labour to look after and pick.
- James' father enjoyed growing vegetables.
- The subsidy on oil seed rape has gone down a lot.
- The EU will pay money if you set aside good quality crop land and do not grow anything on it (a maximum of 15 per cent of all crop land).
- The area's physical conditions are good for growing grass.
- Maize grows well in the area.
- On the crop fields, a 4 year rotation is used: 2 years of wheat, 1 year of barley, 1 year of a break crop (beans or rape).

Figure 8.12 Growing crops on Aspinall House Farm

Figure 8.13 Old farm building which is now a hotel

1. Work in small groups and decide how James should use his 350 ha of land. 175 ha are suitable for grass, but what animals should he keep? 175 ha are suitable for growing crops, but which crops? Read Figure 8.11 and note the main points. Do the same for Figure 8.12. Decide how you would use the land on the farm. Write a short report explaining what you have decided and why.
2. Draw a systems diagram to show how you have decided to run the farm.

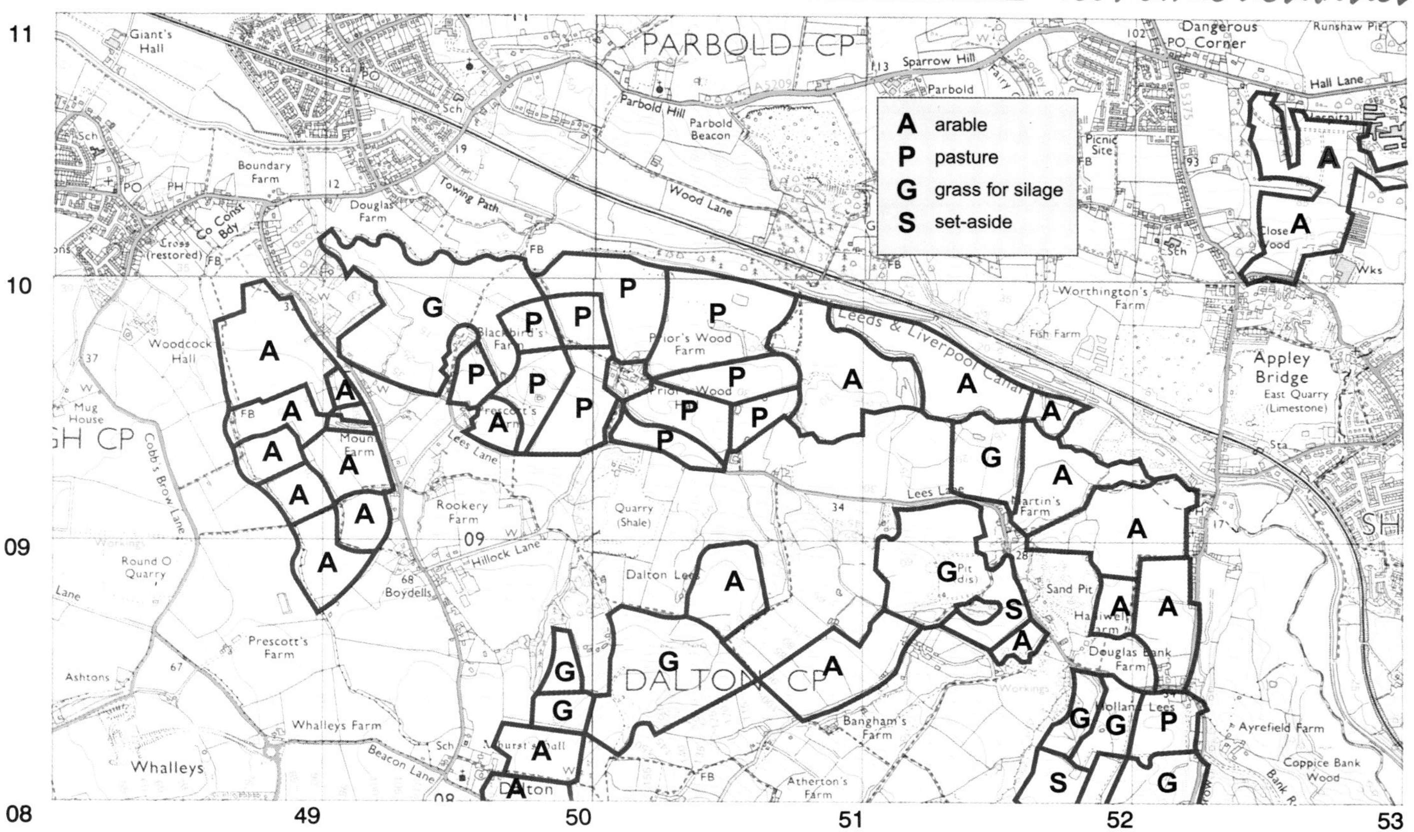

Figure 8.14 The Douglas Valley, north west of Wigan: 1:25 000, © Crown Copyright

A CHANGING LANDSCAPE

The land around Aspinall House Farm used to be farmed by many farmers, each with their own small farm. Recently, many of these farmers have left farming, because they found it difficult to earn money or they retired and their children did not go into farming. This has been common all over the UK.

On Figure 8.14 a number of farms are marked. Many of these are now used for other purposes. Figure 8.15 shows the grid reference and use of these buildings.

3 **a** Copy Figure 8.15 and complete the names of the farms.
b What fraction of the farms still remain as farms?
c Why are so many farm buildings used for other purposes?

4 **a** How high above sea level are: Holland Lees (522 084); Mount Farm (491 095); Prior's Wood Farm (502 097)?
b Is the land used for crops higher or lower than that used for grass? Why do you think this is?
c Why do you think all the fields around Prior's Wood Farm (502 097) are used for grazing cows?
d List other industries on the map and their grid references.
e Do you think that most of this map shows a rural (countryside) or an urban (built-up) area?

Grid reference	Use	Name
495 095	Restaurant	
495 098	Nursery/Butterfly World	
494 092	Farm	
491 095	Private house	
502 097	Dairy farm (part of Aspinal House Farm)	
494 089	Pig farm	
507 080	Farm	
509 083	Farm	
515 091	Road haulage	
515 091	Trout farm	
518 086	Private house	
521 085	Old people's home	
522 084	Aspinall House Farm	
524 082	Farm	

Figure 8.15 Farms on the Dalton Ridge

Manufacturing, a secondary economic activity: a case study of the chemical industry, Mersey Valley

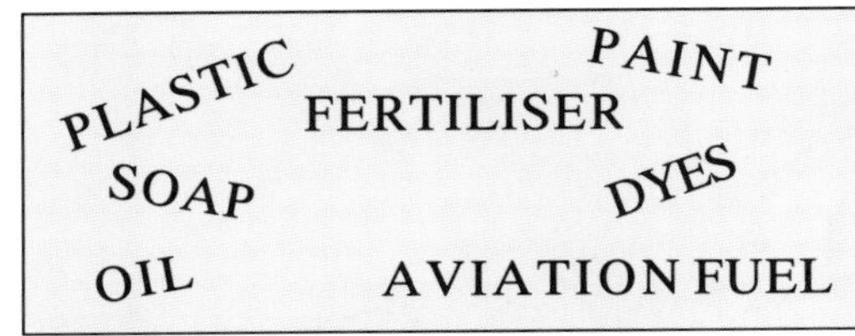

Figure 8.16 Products of the chemical industry

1 The following is a list of things which companies look for when choosing a site for a new chemical works. For each item in the list, finish the sentence that explains why it is important.

- **a** The site should be large because ...
- **b** The site should be next to good transport routes for three reasons, which are ...
- **c** The site should be away from large areas of housing because ...
- **d** Ideally, the site will be next to a large river because ...
- **e** The site should be poor quality land because ...

The Rocksavage Chemical Works at Weston Point are one of many found along the Mersey Valley between Warrington and Liverpool. This area is one of the most important manufacturing areas in the UK, and is a modern version of the Pennines valleys and their textile mills which were so important to the economy of the North West region in the last century. Today many of the 65 000 workers in the North West region's chemical industry work in the Mersey Valley area. Why has this area been chosen by so many companies to build their chemical works?

Chemical companies are like all other types of industry in that they look for an ideal location or place to build any factory. This means that the **site** or piece of land must be right for their needs. It must also have the right **situation**. This means that it must be in the right place to get all the things which it needs (**raw materials**) and obtain workers (**labour**) to make its products. The Mersey Valley has been the ideal location for many different chemical companies making a great variety of different products, as Figure 8.16 shows. Each product requires a different set of raw materials to make it. One set of products is called **petrochemicals**, because it uses petroleum (crude oil) as the main raw material. Others use the minerals available in the region, such as salt, coal, limestone and gypsum and many use raw materials which are from other countries, such as sulphur and nitrates.

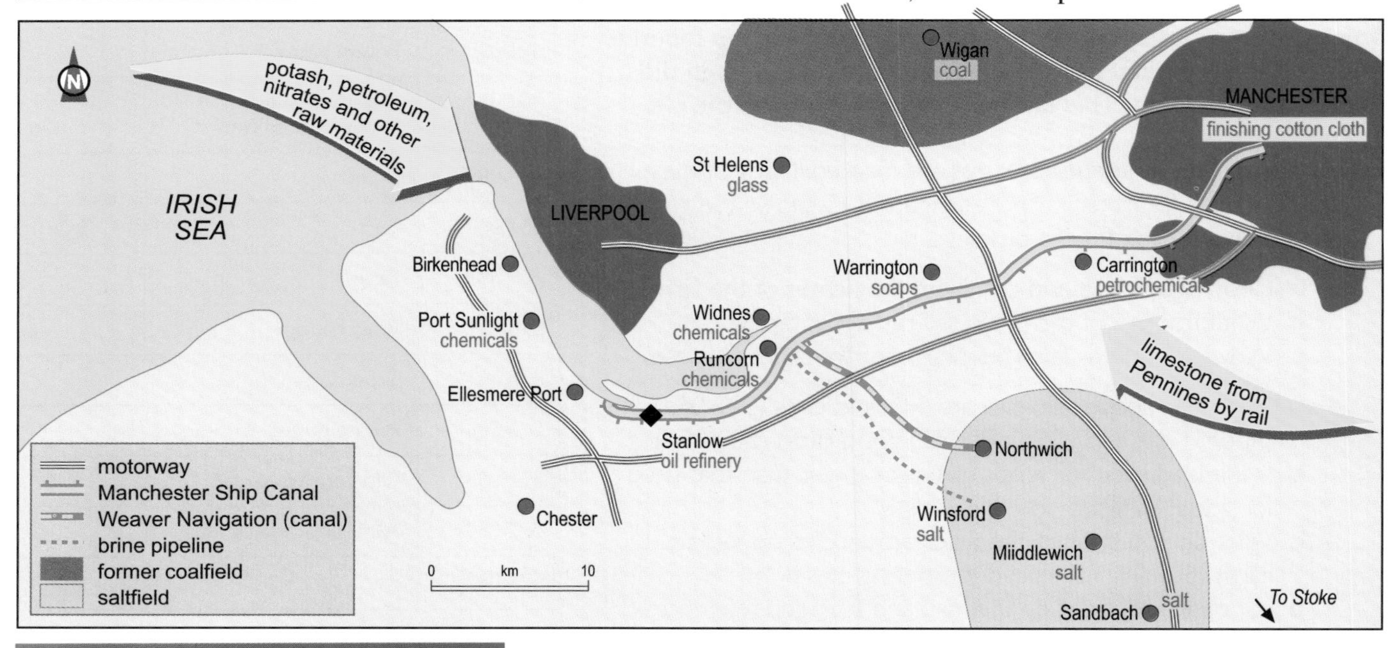

Figure 8.17 The chemical industry in the Mersey Valley

Figure 8.18 Weston Point Chemical Works

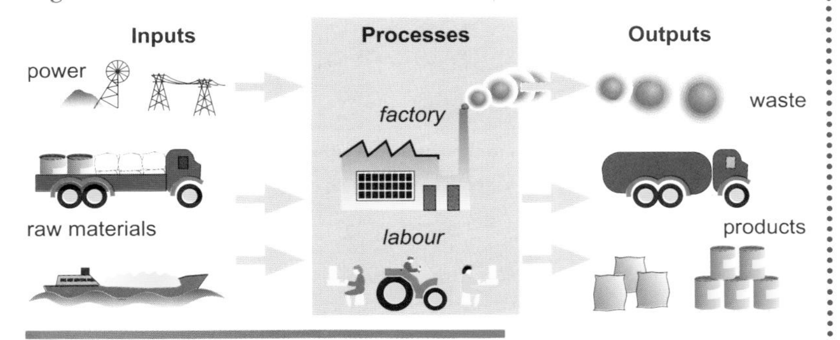

Figure 8.19 The manufacturing system

2 Study Figure 8.18 and answer these questions.
a List four types of transport that could be used to move raw materials and products into and away from the site.
b The following features are labelled A to H on Figure 8.18. Make a list of which feature is shown by which letter. Power Station; Manchester Ship Canal; River Mersey; City of Liverpool; chemical works; housing; lagoon used for storage of liquid waste; farmland.

3 Use Figure 8.18 to make a list of the advantages of the Weston Point site for a chemical works.

4 The map of the Mersey Valley in Figure 8.17 shows where many of the raw materials used by the chemical companies come from. Study this carefully and complete a copy of the table for each raw material shown on the map.

RAW MATERIAL	PLACE OF ORIGIN	TRANSPORT USED

THE MANUFACTURING SYSTEM

A chemical plant is a type of factory making a product out of raw materials (see Figure 8.19). The raw materials and energy are called the **inputs**; the finished products and waste are the **outputs**. What happens in the factory is called **processing**, done by machines and people. If there are lots of machines doing the work compared to people, the industry is described as being **capital-intensive** because the biggest expenditure is on equipment. If there are lots of people doing the work the industry is described as being **labour-intensive** because the biggest expenditure is people's wages. In recent years, many factories have become more capital-intensive. Better machinery is becoming available all the time and is able to do more jobs.

5 What will happen to the number of factory workers as factories become more capital-intensive?

6 Why do company managers choose to have more machines rather than people in their factories?

7 Give an example of a labour-intensive industry and a capital-intensive industry.

Tertiary replaces manufacturing: a case study of the Merry Hill Centre, Dudley

SHOPPING REPLACES STEELMAKING

In the 1970s, waste material from a steelworks was tipped here. Now, on the same spot, you can buy perfume. Round Oak Steelworks used to be the biggest employer in Brierley Hill, a Black Country town in the West Midlands. By 1980, the UK could make more steel than could be sold and many steelworks, like Round Oak, closed – and with it went 9000 jobs. Some of these were steelworkers, but 6000 others were from firms which had done business with Round Oak. Everyone in the community was affected, from the firm which supplied the works canteen with sandwiches, to the travel agency which booked fewer foreign holidays now that there was less money around. Brierley Hill became an unemployment blackspot.

It was an environmental blackspot too with the dilapidated and rusting works and wasteland. There were more than 100 mineshafts left over from coal mining in the early nineteenth century. In 1981, work started on the site and the government made it an Enterprise Zone to encourage new business. This meant that firms could move in quickly (no need to wait for planning permission) and cheaply (no rates to pay for ten years). The land was bought by two brothers, Don and Roy Richardson and they planned a shopping centre – although the first shops were built like factories so they could be converted if the scheme failed!

Figure 8.20 Inside the Merry Hill Shopping Centre

Journey time	Resident population	% of total
0–15 minutes	181 913	4
15–30 minutes	494 894	11
30–45 minutes	1 377 855	30
over 45 minutes	2 487 855	55
TOTAL	4 542 147	100

Figure 8.21 The catchment area of the Merry Hill Centre

1 **a** List the attractions of shopping centres described above and add some ideas of your own.
b Would you like to shop at Merry Hill? Why?

2 Each shopper at Merry Hill spends about £50 on a typical visit. How much is the total amount spent for a year?

3 Figure 8.21 indicates how far shoppers travel to Merry Hill.
a How many live between 15 and 30 minutes away?
b How many live between 30 and 45 minutes away?
c Do these figures seem the wrong way round to you? Think carefully and explain why they are likely to be correct.

Figure 8.22 An aerial photo of the Merry Hill Centre

The Richardsons knew about shopping in the USA and expected the UK to follow suit. Shoppers wanted to be undercover, in air-conditioned malls and away from traffic. A new shopping centre needed to be compact so that it was easy to walk between shops and to get to by car with lots of parking space. A mix of shops with department stores and smaller shops, as well as fast food and entertainment was needed.

Now covering 167 000 m^2, Merry Hill claims to be the second biggest shopping complex in the UK. About 4.5 million people regularly visit the 260 shops and it is a popular day trip for coach parties. On busy days, there is entertainment, e.g. fashion shows, Punch and Judy, and even opera. For disabled people free wheelchairs are available. There is late night shopping every evening, except Sunday, a monorail across the site and a ten-screen cinema. More than 4000 people work at Merry Hill. Most of the jobs are for women and many are part-time.

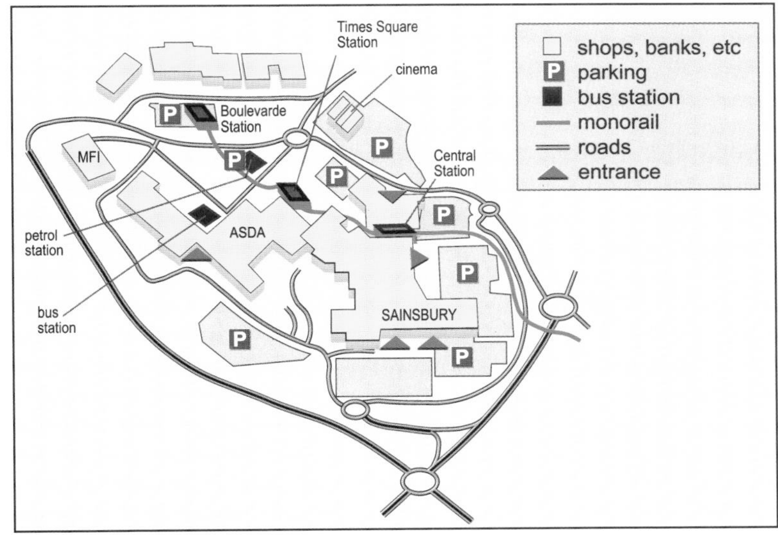

Figure 8.23 Plan of the Merry Hill Shopping Centre

SOME EFFECTS OF THE MERRY HILL CENTRE

A lot of shopping that used to be done in nearby towns, like Dudley, is now done at Merry Hill. Shops have a **threshold population** – the minimum number of customers needed to make a profit. For the high order shops the threshold is high and Dudley no longer has enough shoppers. Soon after Merry Hill opened, Marks and Spencer, British Home Stores and C&A closed in Dudley.

More than 90 per cent of Merry Hill's visitors come by car. There is no railway station and, although there are buses, the travelling time to Merry Hill from only 10 km away can be an hour. There is free parking for 10 000 cars, but the roads were not built to take all the extra traffic created and are becoming congested. There are plans to improve the junctions on the A4036 which leads to the M5, at a cost of £16 million. Who should pay?

4 Study Figures 8.22 and 8.23. Use the plan to help you work out which of the letters A to G on the photograph refers to the following parts of the Centre: Central Station; Times Square Station; Asda; cinema; car park; multi-deck car park; petrol station.

5 **a** **High order** (or **comparison**) goods are usually expensive and bought infrequently. Write down four high order goods which could be bought at the centre.

b **Low order** (or **convenience**) goods are frequently required. Name two low order goods and two shops at Merry Hill which sell them.

6 Dudley is a traditional shopping centre with an open-air market and shops along the High Street. Suggest some changes which could attract more people back to shop in the centre of Dudley.

7 Road congestion in the area could be cut down if more people were persuaded to use public transport. How would you persuade them?

Changing location of manufacturing: a case study of high-tech industry

As was shown on page 47, many companies have been leaving London and moving to other areas. Many have moved to other parts of the South East outside the capital, an area often referred to as the 'rest of the South East' or *Roseland*.

In Roseland, manufacturing jobs as a whole have been declining as in the rest of the UK, but some areas have been successful in attracting new **high-technology** industries. These firms make and design computers, software, semi-conductors (silicon chips) and telecommunications equipment. Most of them spend a lot of time and money on developing new and better products. The majority of people they employ are highly qualified scientists and engineers.

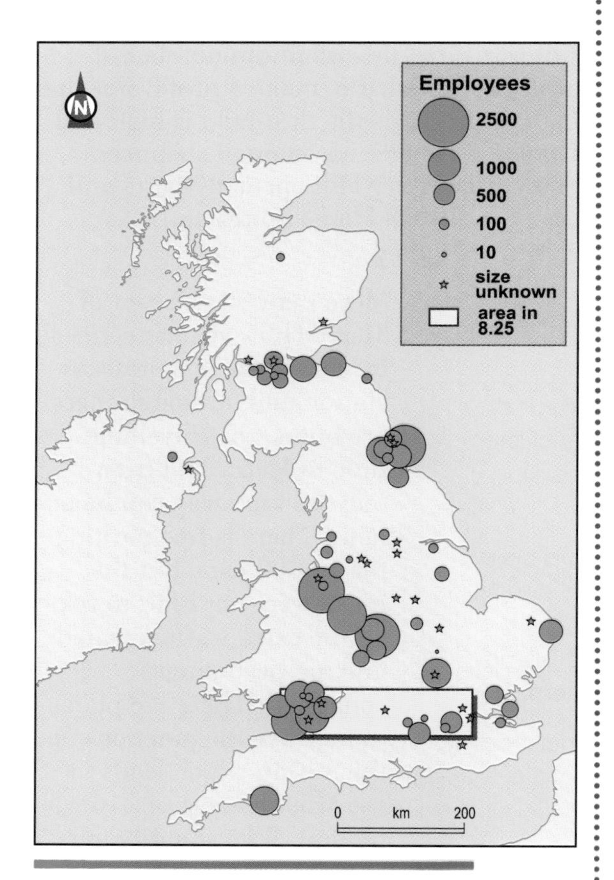

Figure 8.24 Japanese manufacturing companies in the UK

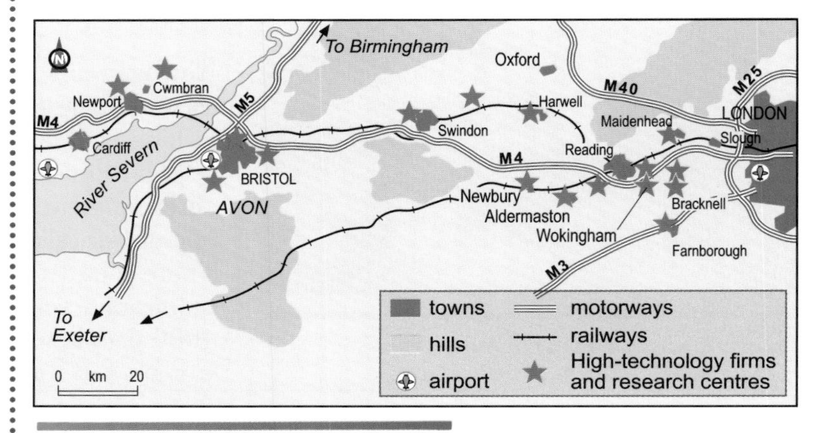

Figure 8.25 The Western Corridor

Unlike the manufacturing industries which were growing up in the last century, these high-tech industries are **footloose** (they do not have to be sited at a supply of raw materials). This means they can be sited almost anywhere. Their highly paid workforce will want a pleasant environment with access to modern communications.

Three areas have developed concentrations of this industry. The Western Corridor is the stretch of land between London and South Wales along the M4. It has many attractions for industries of this type. Silicon Glen is between Edinburgh and Glasgow in Central Scotland and the M11 Corridor stretches from London to Cambridge.

1. Write a definition of a footloose industry.
2. Study Figure 8.25 and make a list of the advantages which the Western Corridor has for locating new high-tech industries. Explain these advantages.
3. Why do you think high-tech industry is employing more people each year in the UK?
4. Many of the high-tech industries in the UK are branches of Japanese or United States companies. Why do you think this is and why do these companies want to build factories in the UK?
5. Study Figure 8.24 and describe where the main concentrations of Japanese manufacturing companies are in the UK. Try to explain why these areas might have attracted these companies.

Changing industrial structure: a case study of the Welsh Development Agency

The Welsh economy grew very quickly in the nineteenth century as many mines and factories were set up. It was in South Wales that the main concentrations of coal mining, steelmaking and other metal manufacturing were to be found. During the 1970s and 1980s, many mines, steelworks and foundries were closed or contracted in size. This had a very serious effect on jobs, and these industries left a great deal of environmental damage, spoilt landscapes and empty buildings. By the mid-1980s, unemployment was very high and there were few new industries being set up.

The Government set up the Welsh Development Agency (WDA) in 1975 to regenerate the economy and improve the environment of the country. It has been doing this in a number of ways: the WDA has been encouraging companies from all over the world to set up in Wales; building new industrial estates so that firms can move straight in; working on projects to improve the environment; and trying to encourage businesses to move to less popular areas of Wales.

no of new projects
0
50
100
150
200
83-4
84-5
85-6
86-7
87-8
88-9
89-90
90-1
91-2
92-3

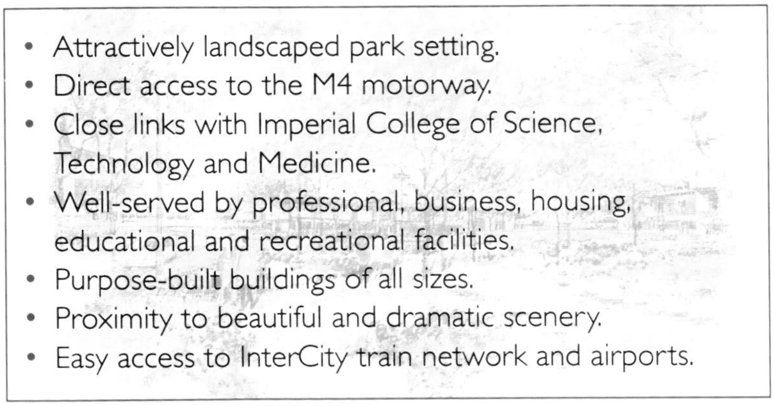

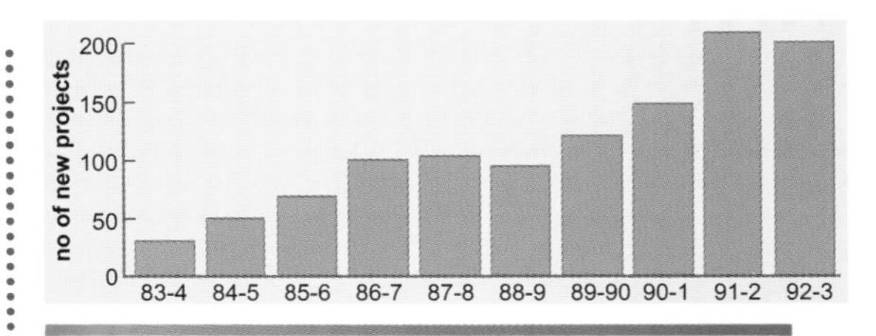

Figure 8.26 Inward investment projects in Wales

manufacturing output 1985 = 100
Wales
UK
90
100
110
120
130
140
'84
'85
'86
'87
'88
'89
'90
'91
1992

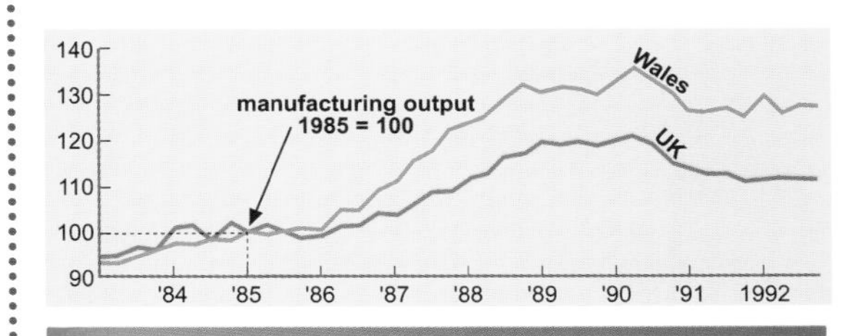

Figure 8.27 Growth in manufacturing output in the UK and Wales

A I million m^2 of modern factory space (the size of 260 rugby pitches) has been constructed for businesses to move into.
B New business parks and industrial estates have been set up all over the country.
C Over £1 billion has been invested by just seven multi-national companies, including SONY, BOSCH, TOYOTA, FORD and BRITISH AIRWAYS.
D Companies setting up in Wales now buy many of their products and services from other Welsh companies.

Figure 8.28 Successes of the WDA

• Attractively landscaped park setting.
• Direct access to the M4 motorway.
• Close links with Imperial College of Science, Technology and Medicine.
• Well-served by professional, business, housing, educational and recreational facilities.
• Purpose-built buildings of all sizes.
• Proximity to beautiful and dramatic scenery.
• Easy access to InterCity train network and airports.

Figure 8.29 Imperial Park, Newport – a high-tech business park

1 Why do you think the traditional industries were closing down in the 1970s and 1980s?

2 Why do you think that many new industries were not attracted to the old industrial areas?

3 Many people were being made redundant in South Wales in the 1970s and there were few new jobs on offer. What do you think many people decided to do?

4 Study Figure 8.26. How many companies invested money in Wales in
a 1983/4?
b 1992/3?

5 Describe the pattern shown by Figure 8.27.

6 The WDA has offices in Belgium, the USA, Japan, Korea and Taiwan. Why do you think they chose these countries?

7 Use all the information on this page to produce a leaflet advertising the successful work of the WDA.

Urban transport problems and solutions: a case study of Glasgow

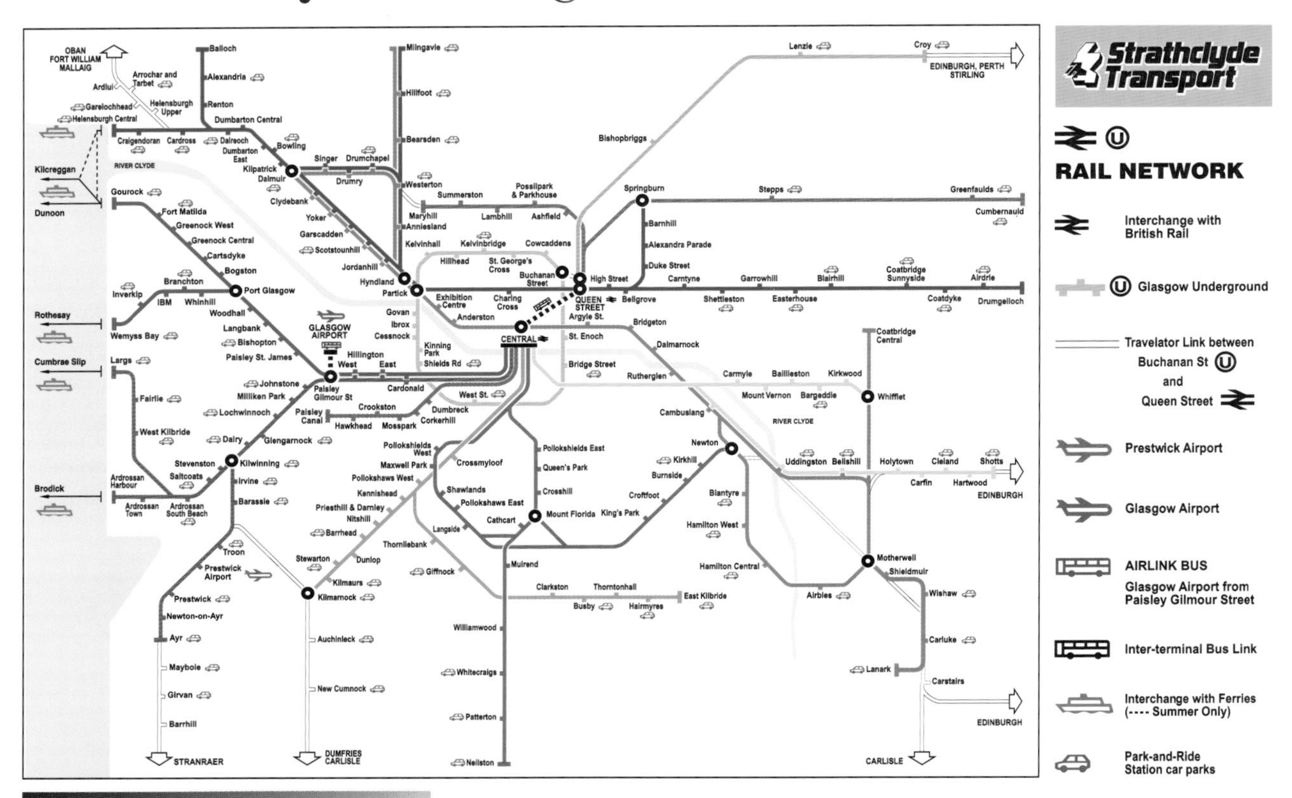

Figure 9.1 Glasgow's rail network

Have you ever wondered why some villages grew into towns whilst others remained as villages? The most important factor is **accessibility**. The successful settlements were where people could easily meet to trade. Glasgow is Scotland's largest city. It is at the **lowest bridging point** on the River Clyde, so routes from north and south meet here to cross the river. The river itself was another important transport route a century ago, with shipping to and from other countries.

The river is much quieter now – but the roads are not. Car ownership in the area has grown more rapidly than the national average in the last ten years. Should more and more roads be built to cater for the extra traffic? Where will the vehicles park?

PAY TO PARK

The council has some control over parking. Within the city centre, the number of parking spaces has hardly increased since 1979, but prices have. The cost of short stay parking has increased at double the rate of inflation and all day parking costs have increased five-fold! This has discouraged **commuting** by car to the city centre but favoured short-term shopping and business use. One side effect has been an increase in all day parking just outside the city centre. Now the council plans to extend the controlled parking area into the inner zone. There will be permits for residents' parking but they will not be free.

> 1 The aim of the parking policy for the city centre is to favour motorists who use their cars outside peak times. Describe how this policy could be operated.

PARK AND RIDE

Parking is provided, usually free, at railway stations around Glasgow. This is to encourage travelling by train into the city. It is called **park and ride**. More than £2 million has been spent to provide facilities. As well as keeping cars out of the city centre, the extra rail tickets sold bring an income of £3.5 million each year. Figure 9.1 shows that there are now more than 70 park and ride stations. Their usage has increased by 45 per cent in the last ten years. About 75 per cent of users drive less than 5 km to the station and 86 per cent are travelling to work. Transport planners are keen to encourage park and ride and also the practice of being driven to the station by someone who then drives the car away. This is called **kiss and ride**. The advantage to the transport authorities is that no car park space is needed. The car can then be used during the day by someone else.

MORE TRAINS

The Glasgow area has the largest and most comprehensive railway network in the UK outside London. Three-quarters of it is electrified. Thirty-eight million journeys are made each year. Eighty per cent of the city centre is within five minutes walk of a station. Six services operate south of the River Clyde from Glasgow Central Station. North of the river, services operate from Queen Street Station. Buses shuttle between the two, but there are two lines which tunnel under the centre of the city, from the north west to the east and south east. These have the advantage of giving passengers a choice of stations in the centre without changing trains. This is also more efficient because time is not spent between journeys, reversing at a city centre terminus station. Glasgow is now planning a new cross city rail link from east to south west, using an old freight line from High Street Station to the lines south westwards from Central Station. New stations are also being built on existing lines and new services introduced on freight routes. Trains from Glasgow to Maryhill and to Whifflet began in 1993.

Figure 9.3 Glasgow's Underground

Figure 9.2 Glasgow's park and ride

CLOCKWORK ORANGE

Glasgow also has an unusual underground railway (see Figure 9.3). Trains are narrow and low. The 10 km circuit is very heavily used, particularly by students, because it links Glasgow's three universities, and also when Rangers Football Club are playing at Ibrox Stadium. Glaswegians call it 'The clockwork orange'.

2 Figure 9.1 does not show places and links in the same spatial way as an atlas or Ordnance Survey map. This is called a **topological map**.
- **a** What are the advantages and disadvantages of drawing a network in this way?
- **b** Using an atlas, or your local Ordnance Survey map if necessary, identify the railway routes in your region and draw them as a topological map.

3 Explain what is meant by: lowest bridging point; commuting; park and ride; and kiss and ride.

4
- **a** What proportion of railway stations have car parks for park and ride commuters in Glasgow?
- **b** Give reasons why money spent on park and ride is considered to be money well spent.

5 Which rail services could be joined together by a new railway link from High Street to the lines which go west and south west out of Glasgow Central (Figure 9.1)?

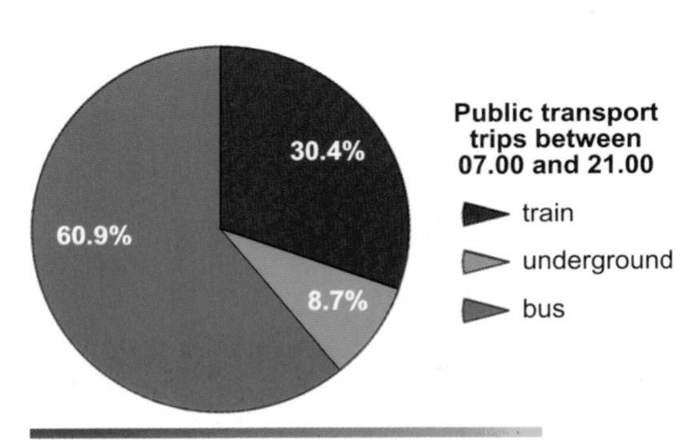

Figure 9.4 Public transport usage

BUS WARS

Figure 9.4 shows that the majority of journeys into Glasgow city centre are by bus. In 1986, a change in the law, called Deregulation, allowed bus services to compete with each other. The Glasgow area now has over 100 bus companies and the number of changes to bus services averages five per working day! Although there are now one-third more buses in the area, 30 per cent are over 12 years old as operators cannot keep fares competitive and afford new vehicles. In the city centre, buses now cause traffic congestion, many of them far from full. The average number of passengers per bus has fallen to 14.

WORKING TOGETHER

The council is eager to promote an **integrated** transport network, with all the providers of public transport working together. There have been successes such as Zonecard, a season ticket valid on almost all public transport in a chosen area, and day tickets giving unlimited travel. As well as bus stations and interchanges where buses connect with each other, the Glasgow area has 19 bus interlinks. These are where buses connect with other forms of public transport (usually at railway stations).

The future will see more bus lanes so that buses can overtake other traffic. Buses will have priority at traffic lights, so by using a transponder, the lights will change to green as a bus approaches. Better information for bus passengers is planned. There could even be talking bus stops, telling travellers how long they have to wait!

STRATHCLYDE TRAM

A new development for Glasgow is **Light Rapid Transit** (LRT) which is to be known as Strathclyde Tram. Line 1 will run from Maryhill in the west to Easterhouse in the east via the city centre. You can see from Figure 9.5 why good public transport is particularly important to many residents of Easterhouse. Each tram will carry 250 people and because they are powered by electricity, they are quieter and produce less pollution than buses. The floor will be the same height as the platforms, making it easier for disabled people to use them. Part of the route will be **segregated** from road vehicles, using old railway routes and part will be alongside or in the middle of roads. Glasgow is planning a network of lines, including the possibility of converting some of its railway routes to LRT in the next ten years. Some of the trains will need replacing by then and LRT will be cheaper than providing new trains.

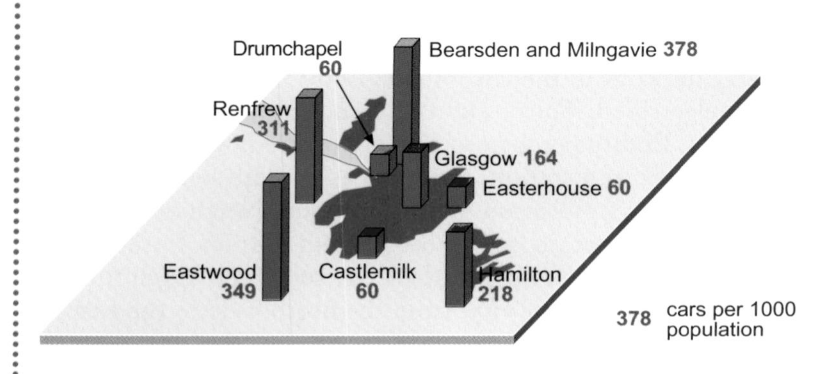

Figure 9.5 How car ownership varies in the Glasgow area

Car	Bus and coach	Motorcycle	Cycle	Rail
67	21	2237	980	3.5

Figure 9.6 Injury risk (killed or seriously injured per billion km)

PEDAL POWER

At present, only 1 per cent of Glaswegians cycle to work. This is likely to increase as more **cycleways** are provided. Already a route from Dumbarton follows the north bank of the River Clyde right to the city centre, mostly using old railways and the towpath of the Forth and Clyde Canal. Figure 9.6 shows an important reason for providing more off-road routes for cyclists. New routes from Paisley and the Ayrshire coast opened in 1993 and from Cumbernauld in 1994. These also use stretches of quieter roads with a special lane for cyclists, or cyclists sharing the footpath with pedestrians.

MORE MOTORWAYS

The least popular part of Glasgow's plans for transport in the twenty-first century is the building of new roads close to the city centre. Glasgow is already unique in having a motorway (M8) through the centre. It crosses the River Clyde by Kingston Bridge, which carries over 150 000 vehicles a day, more than any other bridge in the UK. Improving the road network should reduce the **congestion** which slows down buses. Already the main shopping streets are **pedestrianised**. More roads could be closed to vehicles or made available for buses and taxis only. It is planned to divide the city centre into zones. Cars and delivery vehicles entering a zone would follow one way streets around a loop and be unable to cross into the next zone. Figure 9.7 shows the plan. Only buses, taxis and, in future, trams will pass through **bus gates** between the zones.

It is intended to build new roads to the north and east of the city centre and new bridges either side of Kingston Bridge. On the south side of the river, the M74 motorway would be extended to Kingston Bridge. A spur from the M8, tunnelling past the cathedral would almost complete a motorway box around the city centre.

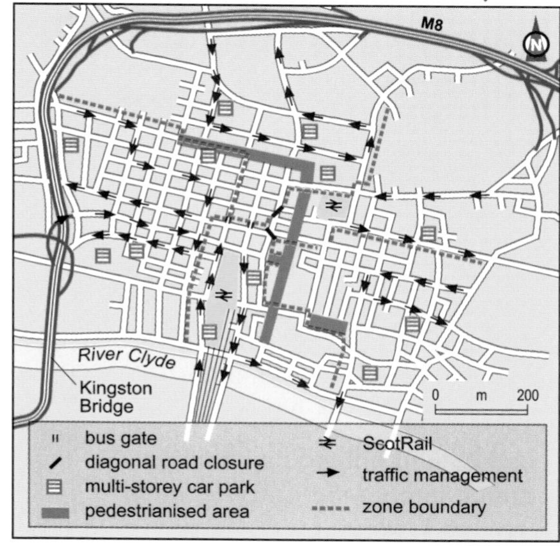

Figure 9.7 Plans for traffic calming in central Glasgow

6 Write the script for a TV documentary which will examine Glasgow's plans a) to improve public transport and b) to reduce pollution in the city centre.

7 Study Figures 9.8 and 9.9. Think about the points for and against the plans for the new roads. Do you think they should be built? Explain, in detail, your reasons.

8 a Which of Glasgow's transport problems are also found in the area where you live?

b Which of the solutions for Glasgow are, or could be, used in the area where you live?

FOR

- Good accessibility is vital if business in the city centre is to prosper.
- Shoppers will enjoy a pleasanter and safer environment if traffic can be channelled round the edge instead of through the centre.
- New roads make some depressed inner city areas attractive locations for new developments.
- Some of the cost will be met by the European Union.
- Much of the land to be used is wasteland.
- The new bridges over the River Clyde will be able to handle an extra 60 000 vehicles a day.
- Road casualties in Glasgow are 50 per cent higher than the UK average. Motorways are safer than ordinary roads.
- Measurements of pollution from traffic in Glasgow city centre streets exceed European health guidelines.

AGAINST

- The cost will be more than £200 million, which would be better spent on public transport in a city where 66 per cent of households do not have a car.
- House values close to the new motorways will fall.
- Motorways act as barriers, separating communities.
- The M74 extension will cross land heavily contaminated with industrial chromium. Excavating for the new motorway could release this pollution.
- The M8 already has many junctions, close together. A lot of local traffic uses it, and there are many changes of lanes which often causes accidents. Completing the motorway box will increase local traffic use.
- The M8 spur will damage a historic part of Glasgow, cutting the Cathedral and Glasgow Green off from the city centre.

Figure 9.8 Glasgow's new motorway plans

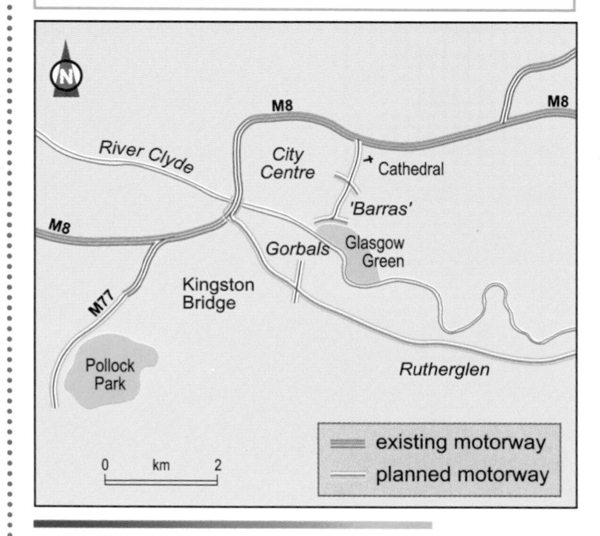

Figure 9.9 Glasgow's motorways

Ports: a case study of Fleetwood

Fleetwood is the second most important port in the north west of England, but two centuries ago it was just sand dunes. The area was owned by Sir Peter Hesketh-Fleetwood. In 1835, parliament gave Sir Peter and his friends permission to build a railway from Preston to Fleetwood. An architect was employed to plan a new town with a harbour in the mouth of the River Wyre.

Loading and unloading boats can be difficult in a tidal estuary, so in 1877, Wyre Dock was opened. Cargoes of grain, timber, iron ore and esparto (a fibre from Spain and North Africa used in making paper) came in and coal went out. However, before long, there was serious competition from the new Albert Edward Dock at Preston, four times the size of Wyre Dock, and in 1894, the Manchester Ship Canal opened, attracting away even more of Fleetwood's cargoes. The dock owners had to look for new business. They persuaded some trawler owners from east coast ports to move to Fleetwood. By 1909, Fleetwood had the UK's most modern fish dock, with trains taking fresh fish directly to all major towns in the region.

Fleetwood still has the best fish handling facilities on the UK's west coast. Sixty-three trawlers operate from here and there is an 800 m quayside area, two fish markets, cold storage and ship repair facilities. Kippers (smoked herring) are produced here. Freight in lorries still passes through the port on its way to Ireland as there is a deep water roll on/roll off (ro/ro) terminal. In summer, a passenger service also sails to the Isle of Man, but Wyre Dock no longer handles cargo. Most modern ships are too large for the dock and a lot of cargo is now sent in containers through specialised ports such as Royal Seaforth Dock at Liverpool. The owners are now turning Wyre Dock into a marina with 350 berths for private yachts. The surrounding land will have shops, restaurants and 700 luxury homes.

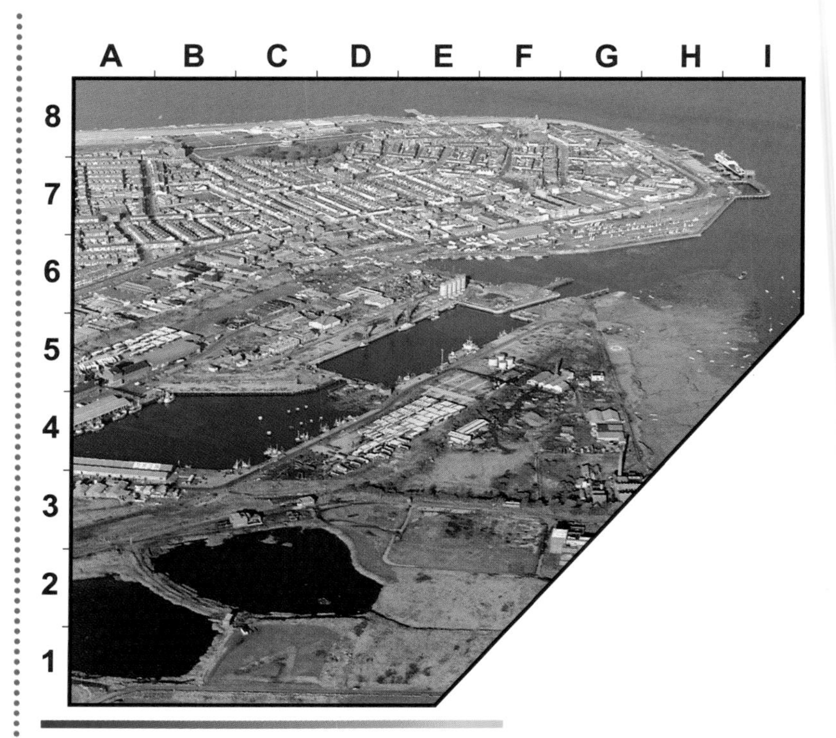

Figure 9.10 Wyre Dock and Fleetwood

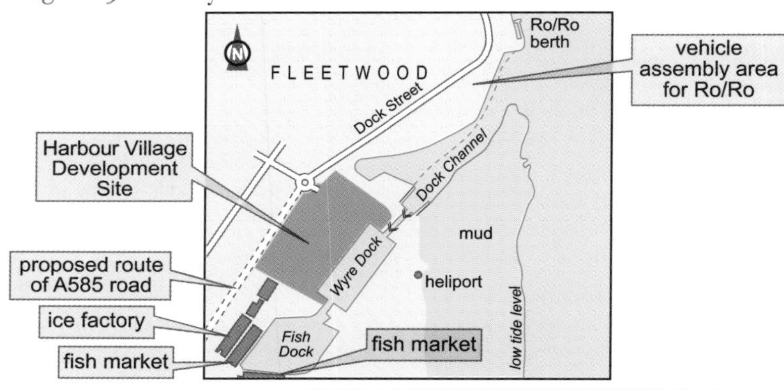

Figure 9.11 The Port of Fleetwood

1. Compare Figures 9.10 and Figure 9.11. In which square is a) Wyre Dock, b) the ro/ro berth, c) the Ice Factory?
2. Suggest reasons why Preston and Manchester took trade away from Fleetwood a century ago.
3. Why do you think passenger services to the Isle of Man only operate during the summer months?
4. You have been given the job of designing the new Fleetwood Harbour Village (grid squares D5 and E6 on Figure 9.10). Use Figure 9.11 and draw a plan of the area with your design. Describe your plan.

BHX calling: a case study of an airport

BHX is the call sign for Birmingham International Airport. An airport site needs a long strip of flat land, preferably away from mountains and in an area where fog is unlikely. It needs good land communications both by road and rail. Business people want the airport to be near to the city in which they trade but residents want it far away from their homes because of noise pollution. No site is perfect, but Birmingham satisfies most of these needs.

The airport is 12 km from the city centre, just ten minutes away by train and close to where two motorways cross.

In the 1970s, the main runway was extended so that modern, larger aircraft could land. In 1984 a new passenger terminal was opened and linked to a new railway station, Birmingham International.

Business has grown, particularly holiday charter flights, as incomes have risen and more people can afford foreign holidays. However, Birmingham's top destinations (Dublin and Paris) are mainly served by scheduled flights.

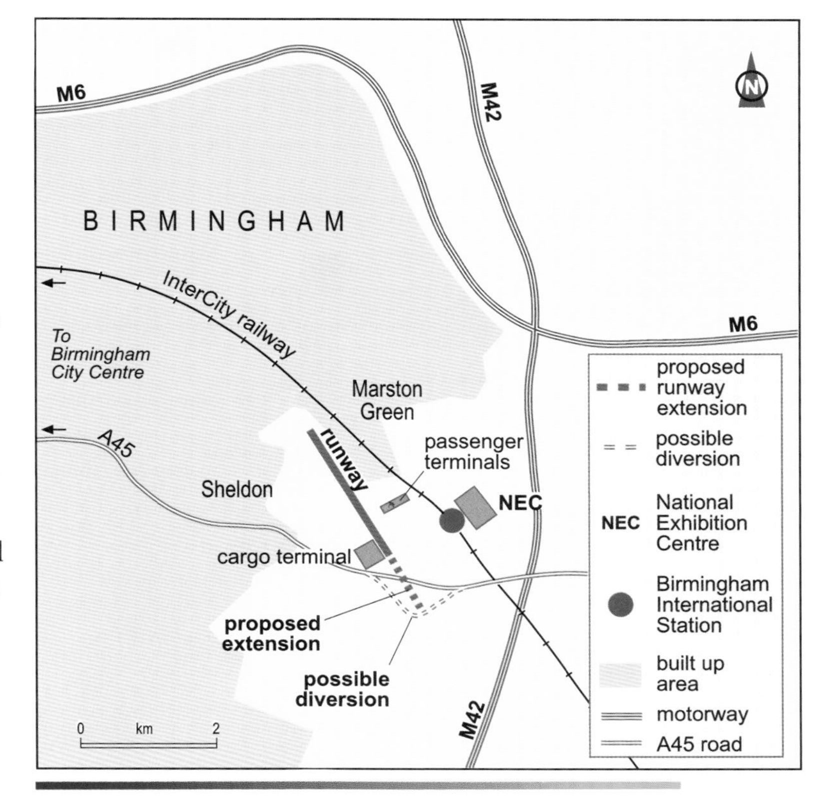

Figure 9.12 Birmingham International Airport location

With 3 million people living within 30 minutes of the airport by car and more than 7 million less than an hour away, the airport authorities would like to offer more routes, particularly to the USA. To do this the runway will need to be extended. The A45 road will need to be put in a tunnel or re-routed, with some trees removed and a hill lowered (see Figure 9.12). A new terminal, Eurohub, was added in 1991 and now 4 million passengers a year pass through Birmingham but by the year 2005 this is expected to increase to 10.5 million.

	International charter	International scheduled	Domestic
Jan	78	84	50
Feb	75	98	57
Mar	88	112	64
Apr	89	128	64
May	199	125	68
Jun	229	131	70
Jul	240	128	70
Aug	245	124	71
Sep	241	153	79
Oct	199	125	70
Nov	93	110	60
Dec	55	107	56

Charter = special flights, usually for foreign holiday companies. Scheduled = regular flights, usually for business people. Domestic = flights within the UK, usually scheduled.

Figure 9.13 Passenger traffic in 1993

1 a List the requirements of a perfect airport location.
  b To what extent does the location of Birmingham International Airport satisfy each of these?

2 Explain the difference between International Charter, International Scheduled and Domestic.

3 a Draw the frame for a bar graph, with 'months' on the horizontal axis and 'air passengers, in thousands' on the vertical axis. Use a suitable scale to take the vertical axis up to 500.
  b Use the information in Figure 9.13 to draw a compound graph. Use three colours, one for each sector – and don't forget a key.
  c During which six months are holiday flights most important?
  d In 1993, which month was the busiest overall?

Network change: Robin Hood back on the rails

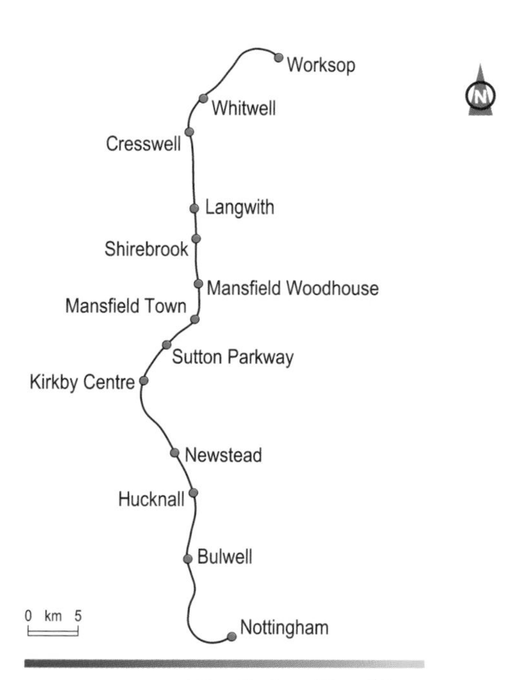

Figure 9.14 The Robin Hood line

On 10 October 1964, a crowd of people at Hucknall, near Nottingham, waved off the last train. It was thought of as the slow and dirty way to travel to Nottingham. Steam engines pulled the trains and if you missed your train, you had to wait up to three hours for the next one! Buses were much more frequent and there were more people than ever before who could now afford their own cars. The government decided that railways which were losing money should be closed.

Now even more people have cars and road **congestion** is worse than ever. Politicians are also more aware that about 50 per cent of the population does not have the use of a car – children, many old people, those not so well off and many housewives when their husbands have gone to work in the family car. Hucknall used to be a coal mining town but in 1986 the last pit closed. Unemployment meant there was less money to be spent and more travelling necessary in order to find work. Nottingham, 15 km away, has a wide range of industries as well as being the main shopping centre in the region. The journey by bus now can take up to one hour. Car users do little better and have the problem, and cost, of parking.

BRING BACK THE TRAINS!

After the stations had closed, coal trains continued to pass through Hucknall with fuel for power stations until 1988, when Linby Colliery, the last in the valley was shut. Fortunately the track was left in place, rusting amongst the weeds (see Figure 9.15). This meant that re-opening the line to passengers would be cheaper than building a new railway.

Figure 9.15 Hucknall Station in 1991

Figure 9.16 Hucknall Station in 1994

Nottinghamshire County Council drew up plans for trains from Nottingham to Hucknall and Newstead. The government had no money available for the line but the council asked transport geographers from Leeds University to study the plan. With road traffic congestion in Nottingham described as 'chronic' and colliery closures encouraging local people to travel further for work, they concluded that fares would more than pay for running the trains and the quality of life for 250 000 people would be improved. The local councils put £6.4 million into it, a small amount compared to the government's £84 million plan to widen 10 km of the M1 motorway nearby.

Figure 9.17 Bulwell Station

In May 1993, trains began to run again, every hour from 7 am until 10 pm. A brick platform with a shelter, a car park and bicycle stands had been built at Hucknall (see Figure 9.16). To keep costs down, there are no staff at the station and tickets are sold on the train. The problem is the trains are so popular that some are overcrowded. Soon after the line re-opened, 6500 journeys a week were being made. Nearly a third of them were on Saturdays so the county council hired another train to provide a 30 minute service on Saturdays.

In Hucknall, there are three Rail Link Bus Feeder Services. Rail tickets include the cost of using the Nottingham City Nipper buses which link the railway station to the shopping centre. In summer, buses meet trains at Newstead and run to Newstead Abbey, Langdale Craft Centre, White Post Farm Park and the Butterfly Centre.

TRAINS RETURN TO MANSFIELD

The success of the scheme encouraged the government to provide £6.5 million for Stage 2, extending the line to Mansfield, the largest town in England without a rail service. Originally, the track continued to the head of the valley and tunnelled under the Robin Hood Hills to Kirkby in Ashfield but when the line closed, the tunnel was filled with waste rock from coal mines. This had to be dug out and, from the north end of Kirkby Tunnel a short new link line was built to join up with the freight railway through Mansfield to Worksop. New stations were built at Kirkby, Sutton, Mansfield and Mansfield Woodhouse. Trains began running in 1995. Stage 3 to Worksop is planned for 1998.

1. Use Figure 9.14 to work out how far it is by train from Mansfield to Nottingham.
2. The bus journey from Nottingham to Hucknall now takes longer than it did in 1964. What is the reason for this?
3. Look carefully at Figures 9.15 and 9.16. Can you pick out the roofs of buildings which are on both photos? What has replaced the weeds which used to grow?
4. Trains through Hucknall use a single track for both directions. Explain why this made the station much cheaper to build.
5. Look at Bulwell station in Figure 9.17. What has been done to identify the station with the Robin Hood line?
6. Nottinghamshire County Council wants the Robin Hood line to be part of an integrated transport system. How are they trying to do this?
7. How is off-peak leisure use encouraged?
8. Give examples of how improving the transport network could improve quality of life. (Clues – jobs, shopping, leisure.)

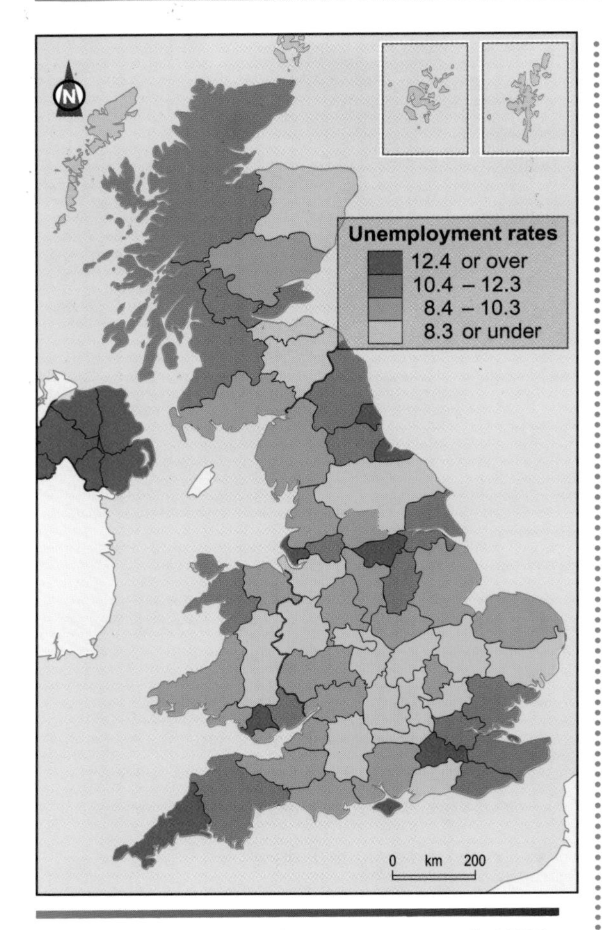

Figure 10.1 Unemployment rate, mid-1990s

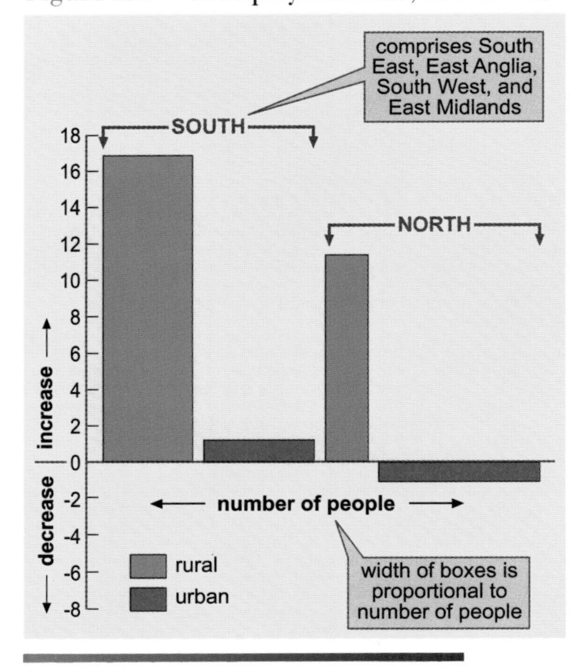

Figure 10.2 Percentage change in employment 1982–1990

ARE SOME REGIONS BETTER OFF THAN OTHERS?

Figure 10.1 is a map of unemployment in the UK during the mid-1990s. This map is often used to show which regions are better off than others. However, it is not easy to point to any one area of the UK and prove conclusively that it is better off than another. The issue is complicated by four factors.

Scale

Areas of real poverty or wealth tend to be small – much smaller than the standard regions in Figure 10.3. The average incomes in the London area, for example, are higher than other regions of the UK, but the average income on some council estates in East London is amongst the lowest in the country.

Change

In the 1980s unemployment levels were clearly higher in the north of England than in the south, creating the so-called north–south divide. This happened because of the dramatic slump in certain industries in the early 1980s, such as coal mining, steel, shipbuilding and car manufacture, all of which were far more important as a proportion of total jobs in the north and Midlands than in the south.

However, in the late 1980s and early 1990s there was a sharp decline in the number of jobs in financial services (such as banks), tourism and defence, all of which are particularly important in southern England. The greatest number of firms becoming bankrupt in this period were in the South West, East Anglia, and the South East.

Urban–rural contrasts

Many of the areas with the highest unemployment shown in Figure 10.1 are larger cities. It is generally the case that cities and large towns suffer far higher rates of unemployment than rural areas. This is because the trend in recent years has been for firms to locate outside cities and towns, and rural areas have picked up the firms that have moved out (Figure 10.2).

Measuring quality of life

Quality of life means how well we live. It is not possible to pick any one measure and use that to prove that some areas are better off than others. Regions with high unemployment such as the north of England may also have much lower house prices and a less crowded environment than the south. Some things cannot be measured, e.g. how friendly people are.

1. Using Figure 10.3, copy the map, devise a shading scale and plot the data given in one of the columns of the table.
   Describe the pattern you have found and explain it.
2. Does the data in Figure 10.3 support the idea of a north–south divide?
3. What is meant by quality of life? Write down six things which affect people's quality of life. Tick those which can be measured easily and cross those which can't.

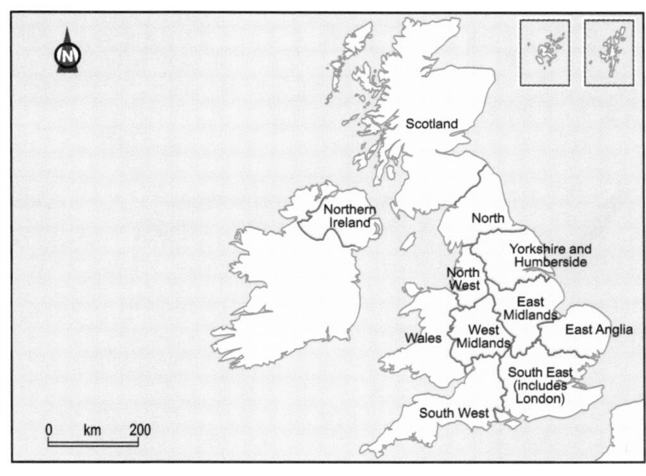

	UK region	Cars per 1000 people	% population change 1981–92	% of school leavers with 3 or more A-levels or equivalent	£ Average total personal income
the 'South'	South East	388	+0.4	20	10 900
	East Anglia	409	+0.9	19	9 500
	South West	401	+0.7	18	9 000
	East Midlands	341	+0.5	15	8 900
the 'North'	West Midlands	377	+0.2	17	8 800
	Yorkshire and Humberside	313	+0.2	17	8 800
	North West	325	−0.1	16	8 800
	North	284	−0.1	13	8 600
	Wales	328	+0.3	14	8 000
	Scotland	280	−0.1	15	9 400
	Northern Ireland	281	+0.4	23	8 000
United Kingdom average		352	+0.3	18	9 500

Figure 10.3 Regions of the UK and data for mid-1990s

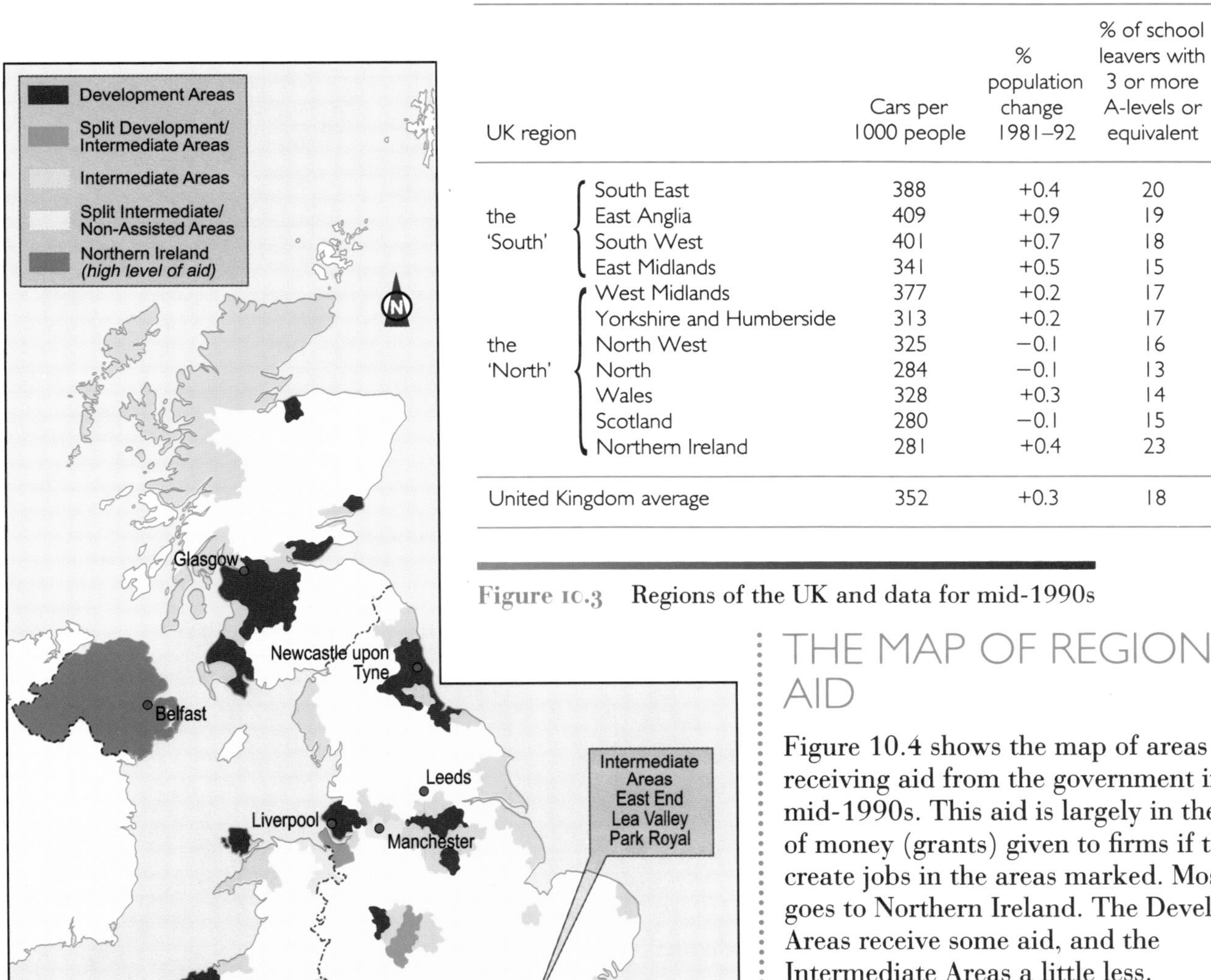

Figure 10.4 Government Assisted Areas in the UK 1995

THE MAP OF REGIONAL AID

Figure 10.4 shows the map of areas receiving aid from the government in the mid-1990s. This aid is largely in the form of money (grants) given to firms if they create jobs in the areas marked. Most aid goes to Northern Ireland. The Development Areas receive some aid, and the Intermediate Areas a little less.

4. Compare Figure 10.4 with Figure 10.1. Do all the Assisted Area places have high unemployment?
5. Are there any areas with high unemployment which do not appear to be Assisted Areas?

Peripheral regions: a case study of Northern Ireland

Northern Ireland is a distinctive region of the UK, cut off from the mainland with its own culture, accent and history. Figure 10.6 shows that it also has high unemployment.

WHY DOES NORTHERN IRELAND HAVE SUCH HIGH UNEMPLOYMENT?

Location

Northern Ireland's obvious weakness is that it is a long way from the main markets of Britain and Europe. Northern Ireland firms have additional transport costs which their rivals do not.

A small market

The population of Northern Ireland in the mid-1990s is only 1 650 000, and the population of the whole of Ireland is only 5 million. This puts Northern Irish producers at a disadvantage compared to, say, firms in London who might have as many as 30 million people within 160 km.

Figure 10.5 Northern Ireland

	UK	Northern Ireland
% unemployed	9	16
% of population under 15 years old	19	25
% of working men in farming	1.9	6.1
% of workforce in financial sector	12	7

Figure 10.6 Data for mid-1990s

Political conflict

Originally Ireland had a largely Roman Catholic population. In the seventeenth century Protestant settlers came from England and Scotland to all parts of Ireland, but over the following centuries it was only in the north of the country that they remained culturally different from the Roman Catholics and were in a majority. For many years the whole of Ireland was ruled by Britain, but in 1922 most of Ireland was given independence, as desired by the Roman Catholics. However, the majority of the population in the north (Protestants) wanted to remain part of the UK, so Ireland was divided.

The border between the two countries was badly drawn and many Roman Catholics found themselves in Northern Ireland. Not only did they feel that a part of their country had been taken by the British, but for some years they were discriminated against by the Protestant majority in the north.

Since the mid-1960s up to 1994 Northern Ireland suffered terrorist violence. While this conflict continued, it put foreign firms off investing in the province.

Figure 10.7 Protestants parading in Northern Ireland

The collapse of traditional industries

As is the case for the UK generally, many important industries in Northern Ireland collapsed after 1960. In fact the percentage of the workforce involved in manufacturing has fallen from 48 per cent in 1960 to 23 per cent today. The worst casualties have been linen-making and shipbuilding.

Linen

Linen is made from flax, a crop which flourished in the wet climate of Ireland. Water power was another important advantage which the region had when the industry was becoming established in the eighteenth century. Scottish settlers invested in new factories and built up overseas exports, so that by 1950 linen made up almost a third of the value of all factory output in the province. The decline of the linen industry occurred because other countries produced cheaper alternatives to linen, i.e. cotton, and artificial fibres like nylon. Only linen spinning remained a viable concern.

Figure 10.9 French-owned Montupet factory, near Belfast, which received grants in 1990 of £19 million to locate in the region

Shipbuilding

The Harland and Wolff shipyard was established in the mid-nineteenth century. It built passenger liners and, during the two world wars, vessels for the navy. At the end of the 1939–45 war over 30 000 men worked in the yard. With the growth of air travel, passenger liners were no longer so popular. Other countries, especially Japan, produced ships more efficiently and cheaply. The yard had to be taken over by the government in 1974 because it was losing money. The number of employees has fallen to 2000.

Figure 10.8 Harland & Wolff shipbuilders

AID FOR NORTHERN IRELAND

Because of its high unemployment Northern Ireland has been receiving aid from the government since 1945. Firms setting up receive grants for building, equipment, and for training their workforce. These are the most generous benefits available in Britain and new firms have been attracted in. However:

- 75 per cent of new jobs were set up within 75 km of Belfast, but the area with highest unemployment is in the west;
- many of the new jobs were in branch plants (branches of a main factory in England or another country), and in the early 1990s the economy was weak and many had to close;
- jobs in the traditional industries have been lost as quickly as new jobs have come in.

Figure 10.10 Ownership of selected consumer goods in 1995 (%)

	Microwave oven (%)	Dishwasher (%)	Deep freezer (%)	Home computer (%)	CD player (%)
England					
North	60	8	81	22	26
North West	57	12	83	22	28
Yorkshire and Humberside	56	10	79	19	25
West Midlands	59	11	84	20	28
East Midlands	57	14	85	22	30
East Anglia	53	14	84	23	31
South West	59	20	87	22	30
South East	56	20	87	24	35
Wales	62	12	85	22	24
Scotland	53	12	79	19	26
Northern Ireland	49	14	70	17	18

Despite the problems faced by Northern Ireland the population is continuing to increase quite rapidly. Most of the people like living there and have a good quality of life. If the violence ceases permanently it is estimated that 100 000 new jobs would be created over a period of ten years in areas like tourism. This is another example of the way we must avoid simple generalisations about places.

1. Look at Figure 10.6 on page 68. What does it tell you about Northern Ireland compared to other parts of the UK?
2. Why does Northern Ireland have high unemployment?
3. Look at Figure 10.10 on page 69. Which region appears to be the best off in terms of ownership of goods?
4. Write down three other possessions that could be used to measure prosperity.
5. Why is a table such as this a rather bad measure of quality of life?

The UK's economic core: a case study of the South East

A PROSPEROUS REGION?

Although parts of this region are not well off, as a whole the South East of England is the most populated, economically important and richest part of the UK. Figure 10.12 gives some recent data.

The South East of England is certainly one of the most important industrial regions in Europe. With 1.1 million workers in manufacturing, it has 23 per cent of Britain's manufacturing workforce. What is more, this dominance is greatest in the types of manufacturing which are growing the fastest: the South East has 56 per cent of the country's jobs in micro-electronics.

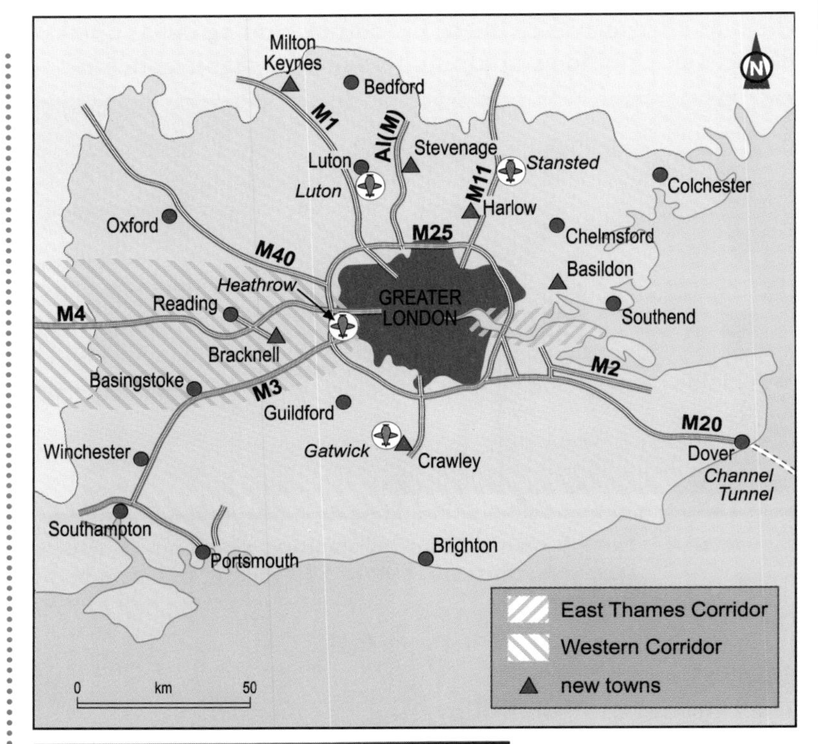

Figure 10.11 The South East of England

	The South East	Proportion of the UK (%)
Area	27 000 km^2	12
Population	17.5 million	30
Gross Domestic Product*	£174 billion	35

***Gross Domestic Product** (GDP) is a sum of all the incomes earned by people and all the profits made by firms in the region.

Figure 10.12 Data comparing the South East with the rest of the UK

Figure 10.13 The cultural heart of the UK: the National Theatre in London

Figure 10.14 The financial heart of the UK: the Bank of England in the City of London

WHY IS THE REGION ECONOMICALLY SUCCESSFUL?

- The South East has a **diversified** economy, i.e. it has not concentrated too much on one type of job. The north of England, for example, relied on coal mining, steel and shipbuilding and when these three declined after 1960 there were few alternative jobs for people to go to. The south east has many types of job, so that if one type vanishes there will still be others available.
- It has more jobs in the **growing sectors**, such as electronics and banking, than other regions.
- It is an accessible region: the hub of the nation's transport network and closest to Europe.
- 35 per cent of the country's population live in the region. It is therefore the region with the biggest **market** for firms selling products or providing services and the biggest pool of available labour.
- It has the **most skilled workforce** with the best educational qualifications.
- Because the region has the greatest concentration of firms, it attracts other firms who want to trade with them. For example, a supplier of electronics components will find more customers amongst firms in the South East than in any other region. Advertising agencies and transport firms come to serve firms in the region. This is called **external economies**.

Although the region is important in terms of manufacturing, it is even more important in terms of the service sector jobs, i.e. office jobs, tourism, education and other services. Many of these, such as schools, health services and local government, serve the local population. Many others are of national importance.

- Because London is the capital city, its location gives the South East 40 per cent of the country's jobs in *central government civil service*.
- *Banking, insurance, finance* – the South East has 46 per cent of the country's jobs in this sector and employs 1.2 million people. Especially important is the City of London (the square mile of offices in the centre of the capital) which earns over £10 billion a year from overseas. This makes it the leading financial centre in Europe.
- *Tourism* – well over 50 per cent of all the cash spent by foreign tourists visiting Britain is spent in London.
- London is one of the greatest centres for *arts* in the world. It has four full symphony orchestras, 40 or so large commercial theatres, two opera houses and 170 art galleries.
- Many firms with branches all over the world have their *headquarters* in South East England.
- The South East has some of the most important *sea ports*, i.e. London, Southampton, Dover and handles over 80 per cent of UK air traffic (Heathrow, Gatwick, Stansted, Luton).

1. In what respects is it fair to describe the South East as a region of world importance?
2. What problems can arise for a region which attracts large numbers of people, both residents and visitors, and large numbers of businesses to locate there? Try to think of examples from the area where you live.

Providing a reliable source of fresh water:
a case study of the North West

Water is called a **renewable resource**. This means that as we use it up, nature provides more supplies. Some other resources are called **non-renewable**, because nature replaces them too slowly and when we have used them up, there will be none left. During summer, with less rainfall, water supplies may not always be replaced quickly enough. People may be forced to use less water, with hosepipe bans introduced. In the North West, unlike many parts of the country, there have been few restrictions in water use even during dry months.

Clean water is piped into most homes by a regional water company and is only really thought about if cut off or it is dirty. These events are very rare in the UK.

The regional water companies do more than simply pipe clean water into homes (see Figure 11.1).

North West Water imports water from other regions to meet demands. About 25 per cent comes from North Wales and 22 per cent from the Lake District. Demand for water in homes is rising with more appliances that use water, e.g. dishwashers.

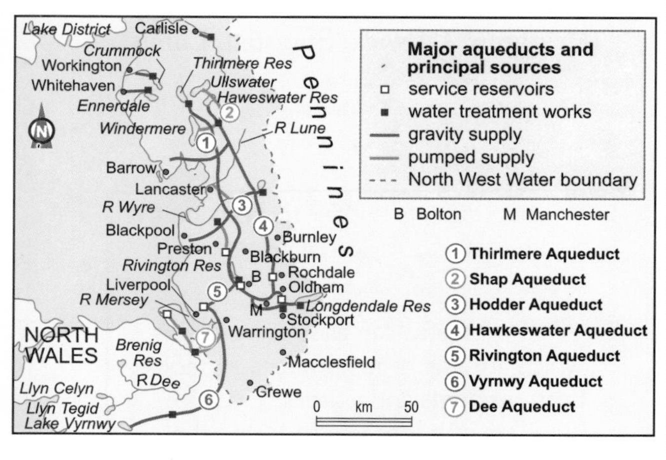

Figure 11.2 Water supply in the North West of England

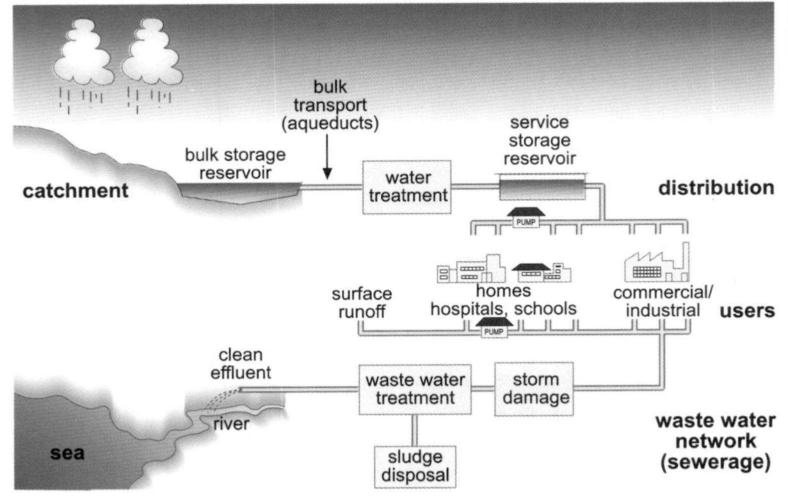

Figure 11.1 The water factory system

1 List ways in which you use water in your home and garden. List other ways in which people use water in the area where you live.

2 **a** Explain what is meant by a non-renewable resource.
b Give an example of a non-renewable resource.

3 Study Figure 11.2.
a Which areas supply most of the drinking water in the North West?
b Is the rainfall in these areas high or low? (See page 16, Figure 4.6.)
c Many of the rocks in the Pennines, Lake District and North Wales are **impermeable**. Find out what this means and how it would help the companies building reservoirs in the area.
d How is water moved around the region?
e What might happen to the rivers and lakes shown on the map in Figure 11.2 in very dry summers?

4 Figure 11.1 shows activities which North West Water carry out in the region. Make your own copy of the diagram, adding examples of activities, where you can. Use Figure 11.2 to help you. Give your diagram a suitable title.

5 **a** Why do you think the regions which supply water to the North West have enough to spare?
b People are buying more and more labour-saving appliances for their homes. Which appliances increase the demand for water from homes?

A new reservoir for Derbyshire: a case study of Carsington Water

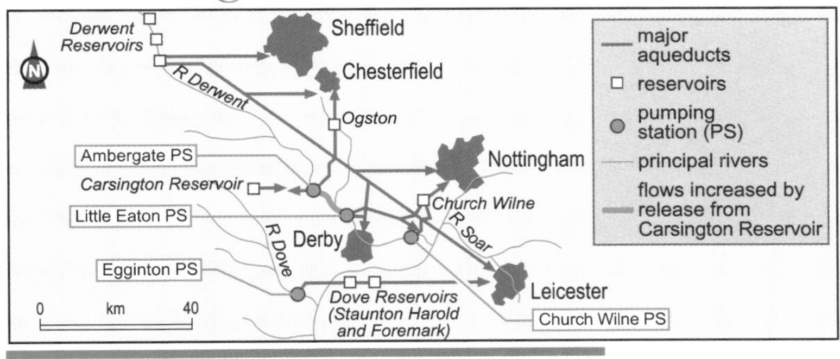

Figure 11.3 Water supply in the East Midlands

Figure 11.4 Carsington, 1994

1 Study Figure 11.3 and answer these questions.
   a From which reservoir or reservoirs do each of the following towns get their water: Sheffield; Chesterfield; Nottingham; Derby; Leicester?
   b Why are there arrows going in both directions between Ambergate Pumping Station and Carsington Reservoir?
   c Why does the River Derwent flow vary during the year?

2 Study Figures 11.4 and 11.5.
   a Describe how the area has been changed by the construction of the reservoir.
   b Do you think people in the villages nearby were in favour of building the new reservoir? Why?

3 Find out the names of some of the other reservoirs which have been built in the UK during the last 10 or 20 years.

WHY WAS IT NEEDED?

The demand for water is rising all the time, and the regional water companies have to build new facilities every so often to ensure that all the water needed is available.

Severn Trent Water completed the construction of the Carsington Water reservoir, the ninth largest in England, in 1991 at a cost of £107 million. The reservoir has increased the amount of water that can be stored in the region by 10 per cent. Three million people live in the cities and towns of Derbyshire, Nottinghamshire and Leicestershire and the reservoir can provide almost one-third of their present water needs, as well as coping with the growing demand.

HOW DOES IT WORK?

Carsington is like a huge storage tank linked to the River Derwent (see Figure 11.3). In winter, when the flow in the river is high, water is pumped along a 10 km tunnel cut through the Derbyshire hills from Ambergate into the reservoir. At other times of the year, when the river flow is low, water is returned by gravity from Carsington back into the Derwent. This is so that there is always enough water at Little Eaton, near Derby, where the water is treated and supplied to the nearby towns.

Figure 11.5 Carsington during construction of the reservoir

WHY WAS IT BUILT HERE?

Seven sites were considered before the government gave approval for Carsington. The site has ideal geography and geology for a reservoir. There is a ring of hills which reduced the length of the dam that was needed. The valley has non-porous clay and shale rocks for the bed of a reservoir. Stone from local limestone quarries protected the face of the dam from wave erosion and filtered the water. Although the new reservoir covers the size of about 700 hockey or football pitches, only two farm buildings had to be demolished.

HOW HAS THE ENVIRONMENT CHANGED?

Two new roads have been built to bypass three local villages. Half a million trees have been planted on the valley sides and new wildlife ponds and recreation areas have been set up. Carsington Water now has opportunities for walking, bird-watching, picnicking, sailing, fishing and horseriding.

Providing a reliable supply of energy: a case study of Rhyd-y-Groes windfarm, Anglesey

Rhyd-y-Groes windfarm has 24 three-bladed turbines and is sited on the hills off the west coast of Anglesey, overlooking the Wylfa nuclear power station. It has been operational since November 1992 and generates about one-quarter of the needs of the island (about 1 per cent of the amount produced from Wylfa).

The UK lies in the path of many weather depressions, which bring with them windy conditions, especially to the west side of the country. In exposed hilly areas facing the coast, winds are high and consistent. These conditions are ideal for the siting of modern wind turbine generators (WTG), (see Figure 11.8). The UK seems ideal for generating this type of electricity which is environmentally friendly.

The government estimates that it should be possible to generate 10 per cent of our current electricity needs by wind turbines. By January 1994, there were 400 WTGs at 21 sites in England and Wales. However, they only provide enough electricity for 250 000 people, or less than 0.2 per cent of the country's needs at about four times the cost of conventional power stations.

WINDPOWER SHUTDOWN

The shutdown of all 67 of National Wind Power's turbines for four weeks in December is expected to cost the company at least £1 million in lost earnings and repair bills. 18 of the turbines were damaged in the strong winds which reached 160 kph in some places.

Figure 11.6 Windpower shutdown

Windfarms damage landscape

A recent application for a windfarm on Anglesey has been rejected by the Welsh Office partly on the grounds of it damaging the landscape. The landscape in many of our exposed uplands is highly valued for its natural beauty and some areas have been designated as National Parks, Areas of Outstanding National Beauty (AONB) and Heritage Coasts, and because of this many people believe wind farms should not be developed in these areas.

Figure 11.7 Windfarms damage landscape

1 Read the articles in Figures 11.6, 11.7 and 11.8 and write a report entitled: 'Why wind power has no real puff', explaining why the government's target for 10 per cent of our electricity to be generated by wind power is unlikely to be achieved. Try to give details of recent changes in energy use.

Family Forced to Leave over Windfarm Drone

A family is being forced to leave its home because of the noise from a neighbour – a windfarm. Their cottage has superb views over the coast and the Snowdonian mountains, but they have sold it to a farmer and are leaving. Their lives have become intolerable since the windfarm came into operation. One turbine is 350 m from their bedroom and six more are within 650 m. A continuous low-frequency droning noise disrupts sleep and makes it impossible to enjoy the garden.

Figure 11.8 Family forced to leave over windfarm drone

Managing the rural environment: a case study of open-cast mining in the Brecon Beacons

For any new development to take place in a national park, the National Park Planning Authority has to give permission.

On this page there are details of a plan which has been put to the Brecon Beacons National Park for approval. Do you think it should be allowed or not?

PLANNING APPLICATION

Applicant: British Coal Open-cast Executive.
Location: Brynhenllys, in the foothills of the Black Mountains, Brecon Beacons National Park.
Development: Open-cast coal mine on borders of the national park, 30 ha inside park, 230 ha in total.

There have been lots of similar applications in South Wales since nearly all the underground coal mines have been closed. Each application has brought strong objections from local communities who feel that the environment will be damaged.

Open-cast mining of coal in this area has taken place before and the sites have now been restored to agriculture or forestry. Open-cast mining is cheaper than underground mining with no need for expensive tunnels and cutting equipment; the top surface is simply removed to get at the coal.

This will be the only open-cast coal mining in any British national park. The site contains over 1 million tonnes of Peacock Seam anthracite coal, which is considered to be the best quality in the world. Seventy people will be employed at the mine and 70 more jobs will be created in companies which supply the mine and service its equipment.

The site will be visible from moorland and hills (see Figure 11.10), which are popular parts of this beautiful landscape and popular walking routes for visitors. It will take about six months to build the necessary roads and other services before mining starts. The mine should be in operation for five and a half years. The company will then spend one and a half years restoring the site to its previous condition.

Much of the site will be used to store the top layer of soil and rock stripped off the coal seam during mining and replaced afterwards. The coal will then be loaded into lorries and driven down local roads, one of which will be built specially, to a cleaning and sorting site about 14.5 km away. Three or four lorries an hour will make the journey between the sites from the hours of 7 am and 6 pm on weekdays.

1. Read the information about the proposal. Make a list of the good and bad things about the plans from the point of view of the national park.
2. Write a reply to the people who have placed the planning application. You must say whether you will allow the scheme to go ahead or not and explain your decisions.

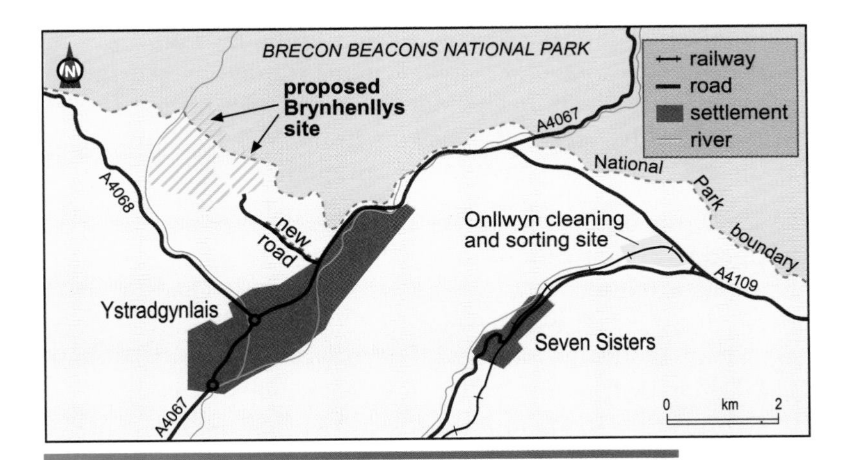

Figure 11.9 Location of proposed mine at Brynhenllys

Figure 11.10 The landscape at Brynhenllys

The causes and effects of water pollution: a case study of the River Mersey

The Mersey was once a clean and beautiful river. Fishing was an important industry and salmon could be caught in Manchester up to the end of the eighteenth century. This was the time of the Industrial Revolution and rapid urban growth. Today, the Mersey is the most polluted major river in the UK, but things are changing for the better.

The Mersey River basin contains a large part of Cheshire, with its dairy farms; south Lancashire, with its arable farms; and some sheep farming areas of Derbyshire, as well as the large built-up and industrial areas of Merseyside and Greater Manchester. The total drained area is 4500 km^2 and more than 5 million people live there.

Manchester was the centre of the cotton textile industry, with the dyeing, bleaching and finishing factories. These industries all used huge amounts of water and produced large amounts of unwanted waste. Dyes were made to colour the cloth and the waste from the process discharged into the rivers around Manchester. A large chemical industry grew up in the valley. By 1902, 445 manufacturers were discharging **effluent** (liquid chemical waste) into the Mersey and its tributary, the Irwell. 52 53

As the industries grew, people moved to the towns to work in the factories and the mines of the south Lancashire coalfield. The growing towns used an increasing amount of water and then returned it, polluted, into the rivers which were regarded as convenient outlets for all waste. Many of the rivers, such as the Irk and Medlock in Manchester, became virtual rivers of sewage. Liverpool discharged all its sewage straight into the Mersey estuary.

It was not until after the 1939–45 war that some efforts were made to control river pollution. In 1951, an Act of Parliament limited the discharge of harmful effluents into the river. From then on, there has been a gradual improvement in the quality of the rivers in the Mersey Basin as more laws have been passed.

Source	Cause	Pollutants
Industry	accidental spillages or deliberate dumping	ammonia toxic substances various chemicals
Farms	accidental spillages or deliberate dumping or soaking through the soil into rivers	cattle slurry dairy washings sheep dip fertilisers agro-chemicals silage waste
Disused mines and waste tips	steady flow underground into rivers	metals various chemicals
Domestic	inadequate sewers and sewage treatment works wrong connections at homes	untreated sewage other domestic waste

Figure 11.11 The causes and effects of river pollution

In 1980, a 15 year programme of works aimed at cleaning up the Mersey estuary was set up. This included a reduction in the amount of industrial and domestic waste which was allowed to be pumped into the rivers in the Basin, the building of new water treatment works and an education programme to tell people how they could prevent water pollution. In 1985, the Mersey Basin Campaign was launched. This was a £4 billion scheme funded by central government to clean up the Mersey and its tributaries. Its target is that by 2010 all the rivers in the Mersey Basin will be Class 1 (good) or Class 2 (fair) in quality.

By 1989, the organic pollution levels on the estuary had dropped to 70 per cent of their 1972 level. Oxygen levels in the rivers are improving and fish are returning. Over 50 species have been observed since 1976, but only four of them appear in significant numbers. North West Water is spending £2.7 billion during the 1990s on waste water services to make up for the years of neglect and to bring the rivers and bathing waters up to the high standards required by the latest UK and EU laws.

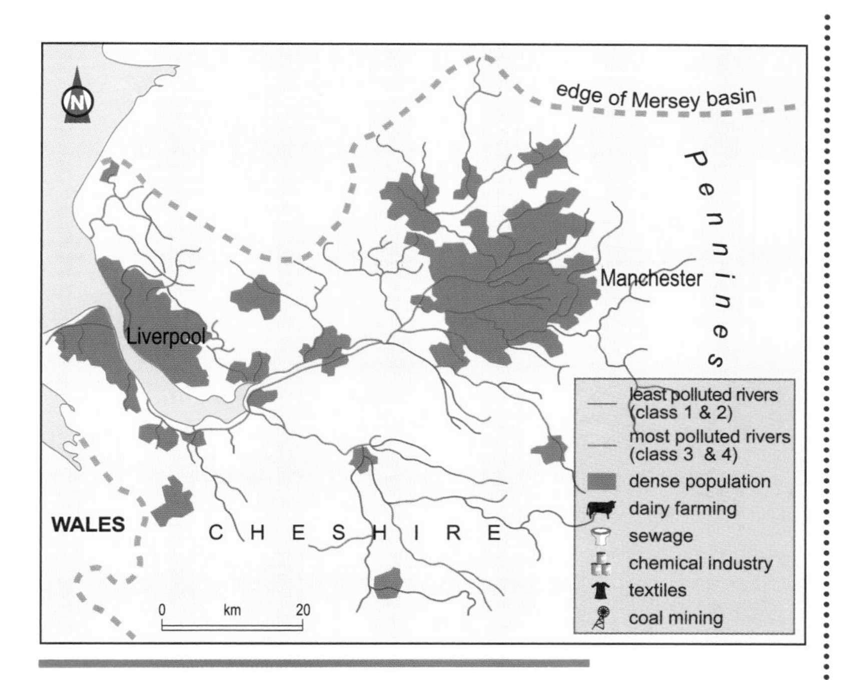

Figure 11.12 Water quality in the Mersey basin

Pollutants in rivers are of two main types:

- toxins or poisons which harm living organisms in rivers;
- organic pollution, such as sewage and farm effluent remove too much dissolved oxygen from the water, so that there is not enough for fish or the organisms on which they feed.

Figure 11.13 Two types of pollutants

1. Read the information on these pages about river pollution. Make a tracing of the map in Figure 11.12 and give it the title 'Pollution map of the Mersey Basin'.
   - **a** Use the symbols given in the key to complete your map by placing them where you think that type of river pollution will be taking place.
   - **b** Use Figure 8.17 on page 52 to add symbols showing the position of the main towns involved in the chemical industry.
2. Read Figure 11.13 about the types of pollution in rivers. Copy out Figure 11.11 and add a fourth column to show which type of pollution will result from the different pollutants in the third column.
3. The National Rivers Authority (NRA) is responsible for pollution control and employs Pollution Control Officers to carry out much of this work. Read Figure 11.15 which shows the five different ways in which they are attempting to do their job. Write a diary of a typical week for a Pollution Control Officer.

Figure 11.14 Pollution on the River Mersey

How the National Rivers Authority controls pollution

- All discharges to rivers in England and Wales from industry or sewage treatment works require the permission of the NRA.
- Other discharges are illegal (except in some emergency cases) and the NRA prosecutes offenders when necessary.
- NRA Pollution Control Officers take regular samples of effluents which are checked at their laboratories.
- NRA staff work hard to prevent pollution wherever possible, pointing out potential hazards at all types of site.
- NRA Pollution Control Officers also respond to spillages into rivers giving expert advice in reducing the worst effects of a pollution incident.

Figure 11.15 How the National River Authority controls pollution

Sustainable development and environmental stewardship: is London a sustainable city?

In 1993, at the Earth Summit in Rio de Janeiro, many of the world's governments, including ours, signed a pledge to make a more efficient and responsible use of the world's resources. This was called **sustainability**. The idea behind it is that we should not damage the environment in a way that makes it unable to recover.

If we are to ensure that the world we live in is here, in a similar form, for our children and grandchildren, we must make sure that our lifestyles are not damaging the globe.

An investigation into the lifestyle of the population of London will show us that our towns and cities are a drain on many of the world's resources. Some experts think that, if a wall was built around London and nothing allowed to enter or leave, the city would 'die' inside a week. Figure 11.21 shows some of the effects that London has on the world's environment, and on the next page there is a detailed study about the effect of air quality.

Study Figure 11.16.

1. Do you think London is using the environment in a sustainable way?
2. Some schemes to improve the sustainability of the city have been included at the bottom of the diagram. Use these, and any other ideas that you have, to write a report entitled 'How London can be part of a sustainable environment'. In this report, you should suggest ways of improving waste disposal, electricity demands, transport, food supply and any other issues which you feel are important so that London is a more environmentally friendly city.

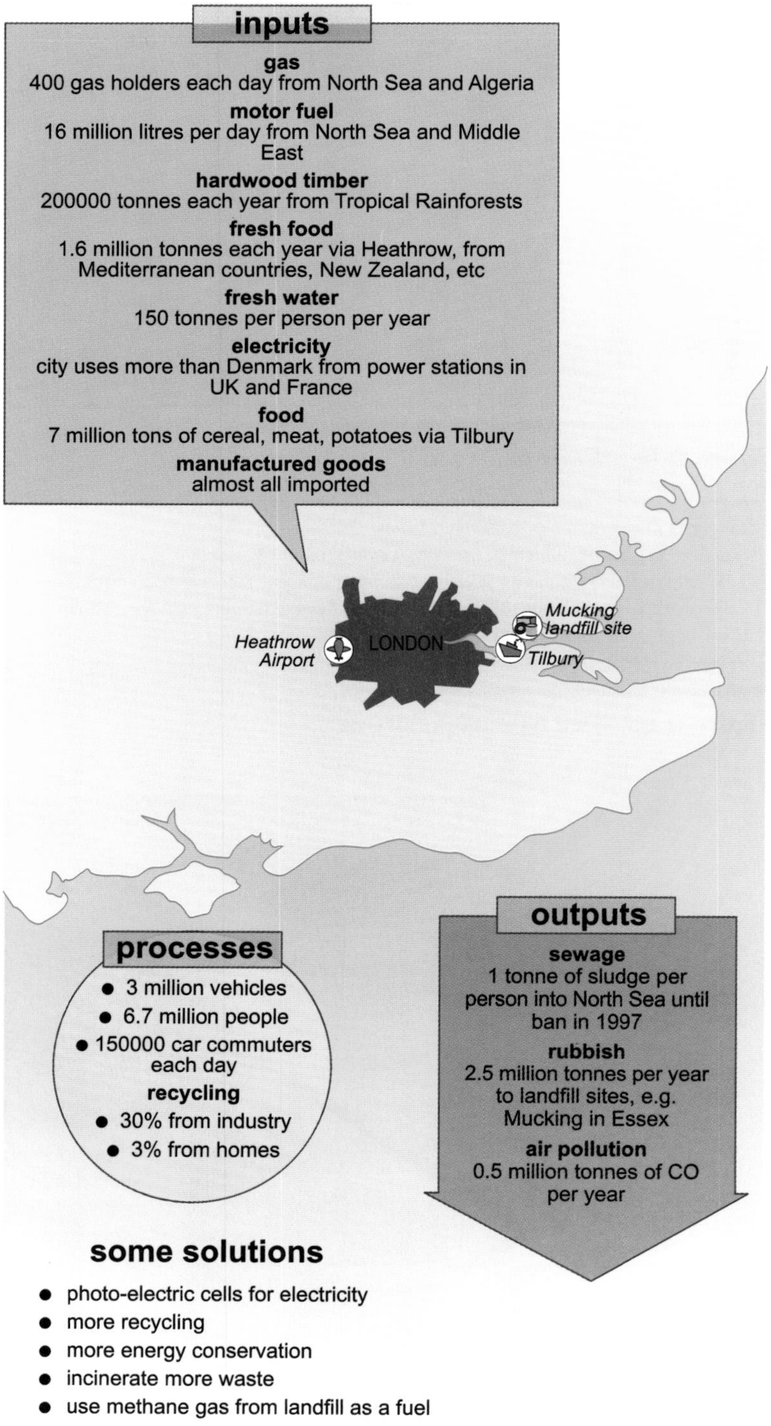

inputs

gas
400 gas holders each day from North Sea and Algeria

motor fuel
16 million litres per day from North Sea and Middle East

hardwood timber
200000 tonnes each year from Tropical Rainforests

fresh food
1.6 million tonnes each year via Heathrow, from Mediterranean countries, New Zealand, etc

fresh water
150 tonnes per person per year

electricity
city uses more than Denmark from power stations in UK and France

food
7 million tons of cereal, meat, potatoes via Tilbury

manufactured goods
almost all imported

Heathrow Airport
LONDON
Mucking landfill site
Tilbury

processes

- 3 million vehicles
- 6.7 million people
- 150000 car commuters each day

recycling

- 30% from industry
- 3% from homes

outputs

sewage
1 tonne of sludge per person into North Sea until ban in 1997

rubbish
2.5 million tonnes per year to landfill sites, e.g. Mucking in Essex

air pollution
0.5 million tonnes of CO per year

some solutions

- photo-electric cells for electricity
- more recycling
- more energy conservation
- incinerate more waste
- use methane gas from landfill as a fuel

Figure 11.16 London's demands on the environment

Air quality: a case study of London

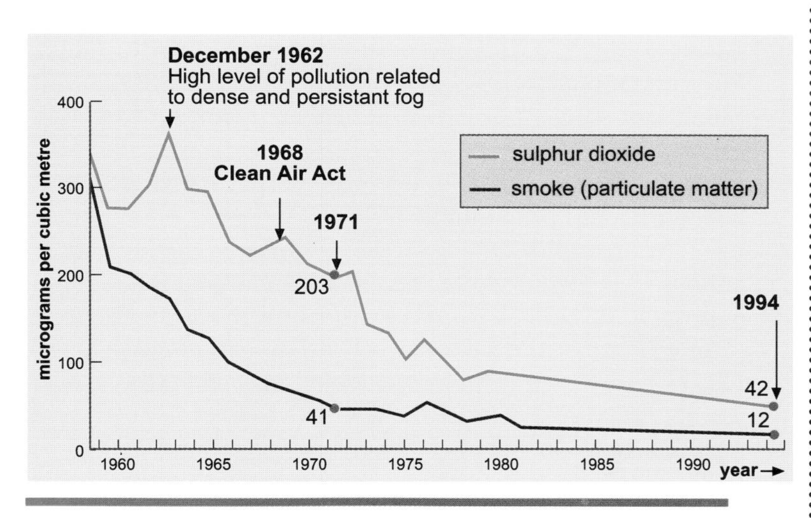

Figure 11.17 Air pollution levels in central London in winter

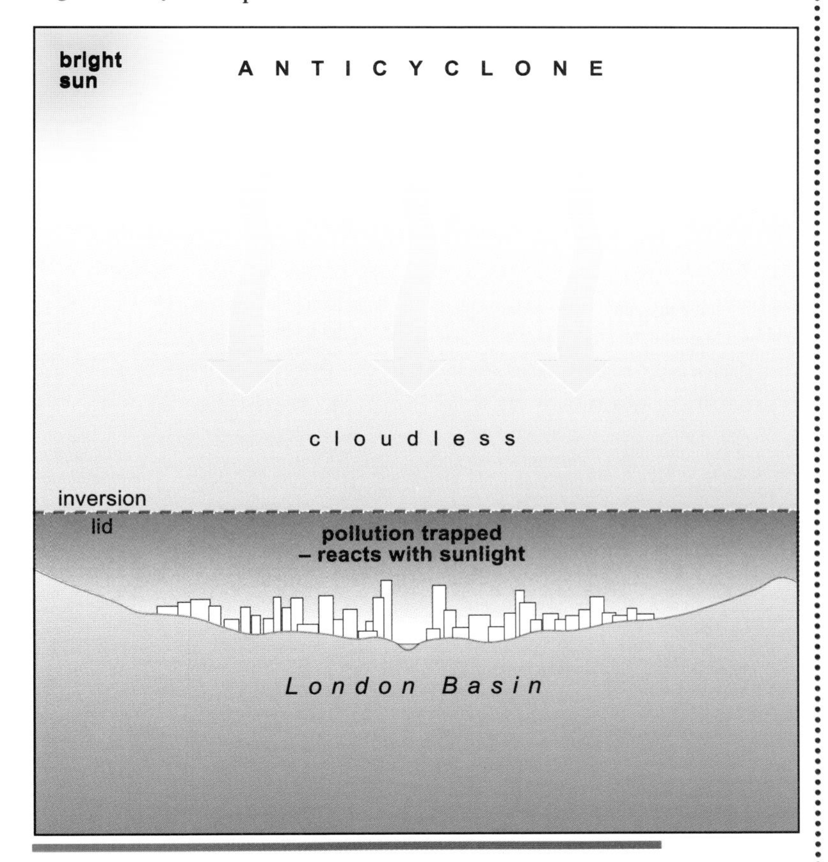

Figure 11.18 Ideal conditions for photochemical smog

Coal burning smog is no longer a problem as the Clean Air Act of 1956 prevented people from burning coal. The only serious polluters are the coal burning power stations, which emit sulphur dioxide. This gas can become dilute sulphuric acid in rainwater. This is what we know as **acid rain**, which eats away at buildings and kills plants.

In most of the UK, air quality is something which affects many people, but it causes most concern in the cities. The weather forecasters even warn us of where and when we can expect poor air quality. In some ways, the situation has been improving in recent years, while in others it has been getting worse.

THE IMPROVING SITUATION

Before 1956, most homes in London burned coal for heating. Coal burning produced sulphur dioxide and soot. In winter, these helped to produce **smog** – a dense white fog.

Smog formed in winter when conditions were cold and calm and water droplets condensed around the particles of soot. In December 1952, a smog lasted without interruption for four days: people could only see a few metres ahead of them, and traffic came to a standstill. Four thousand Londoners died of illnesses brought on by the killer smog.

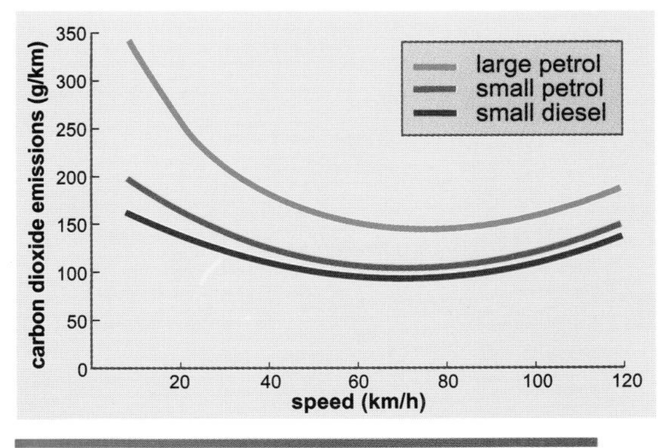

Figure 11.19 Carbon dioxide emissions by vehicle and speed

1 Figure 11.17 on page 79 shows how the levels of pollution caused by burning coal have been changing.
   a Describe the pattern which this graph shows.
   b What effect did the Clean Air Act of 1968 have?

2 Study Figure 11.19.
   a Which type of vehicle gives off the least CO_2?
   b At what speed do vehicles give off the least CO_2?

3 Write a report explaining how the following three changes could affect the air quality in London:
   a greater use of public transport;
   b greater use of bicycles;
   c moving people and jobs out of London.

THE DETERIORATING SITUATION

Pollution caused by vehicle exhaust fumes is increasing, especially in London. The main pollutants are:

- carbon dioxide (CO_2) and carbon monoxide (CO), which enter the bloodstream when breathed in. They make the blood less efficient at carrying oxygen, leading to drowsiness;
- nitrogen dioxide (NO_2) irritates the lungs, causing bronchitis and pneumonia;
- ozone is created by the reaction of nitrogen oxides with sunlight. At ground level, ozone is dangerous: it produces asthma and reduces resistance to respiratory infections. Ozone is one of the causes of **photochemical smog** (see Figure 11.18) – a yellow mist which attacks lungs, stone, plastic and metals;
- hydrocarbons such as benzene can cause cancer;
- lead causes damage to the brain, but lead levels have been falling since the introduction of unleaded petrol in 1985.

Compared to their body weight, children inhale more air, and thus pollution, than adults. Their airways are narrower so that irritation due to air pollution is more likely to produce breathing problems. The number of hospital admissions for childhood asthma in London increased five-fold from 1980 to 1990.

Air pollution becomes trapped near to the ground when anticyclones or high pressure covers cities, especially if they are surrounded by high land, as London is. When these conditions continue for several days, the air quality gets worse and people are warned about it (see Figure 11.17).

Figure 11.20 Air pollution in London